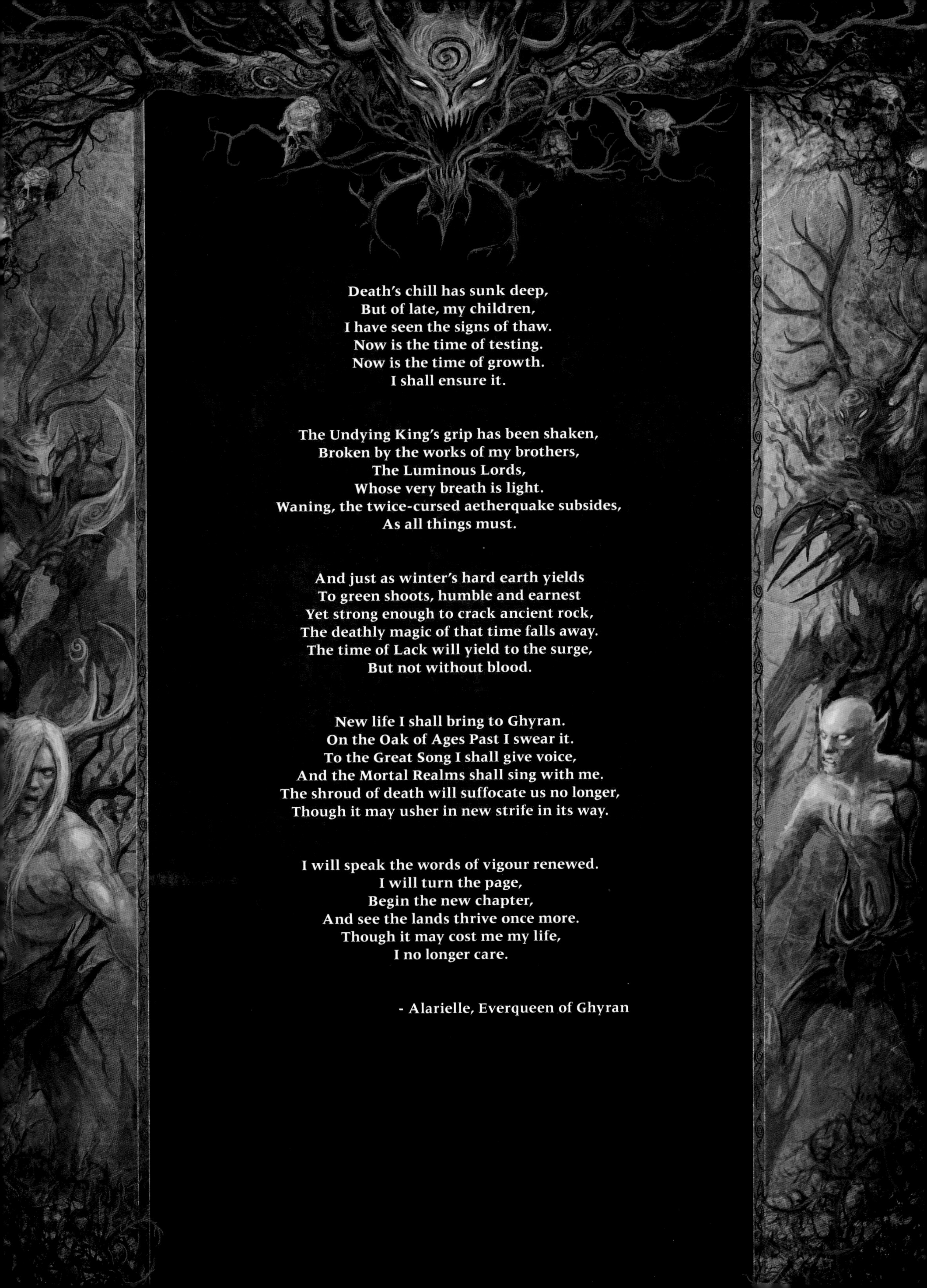

Death's chill has sunk deep,
But of late, my children,
I have seen the signs of thaw.
Now is the time of testing.
Now is the time of growth.
I shall ensure it.

The Undying King's grip has been shaken,
Broken by the works of my brothers,
The Luminous Lords,
Whose very breath is light.
Waning, the twice-cursed aetherquake subsides,
As all things must.

And just as winter's hard earth yields
To green shoots, humble and earnest
Yet strong enough to crack ancient rock,
The deathly magic of that time falls away.
The time of Lack will yield to the surge,
But not without blood.

New life I shall bring to Ghyran.
On the Oak of Ages Past I swear it.
To the Great Song I shall give voice,
And the Mortal Realms shall sing with me.
The shroud of death will suffocate us no longer,
Though it may usher in new strife in its way.

I will speak the words of vigour renewed.
I will turn the page,
Begin the new chapter,
And see the lands thrive once more.
Though it may cost me my life,
I no longer care.

- Alarielle, Everqueen of Ghyran

CONTENTS

DRAMATIS PERSONAE . . 3

THE RITE OF LIFE 4

ACT I – IN EXCELSIS . . 13
- Bestial Wilderness 14
- Brink of Destruction 16
- Tumult Arcana 18
- Tensions Run High 20
- Something Rotten in Excelsis . 22
- They Came From Below 24
- Charge of the Knights Excelsior 26
- From a Dark, Unholy Union . . 28

ACT II – THE RAMPAGE OF KRAGNOS 31
- The Coast of Tusks 32
- Kragnos, the End of Empires . . 34
- The Rise of Kragnos 38
- Skragrott's Muster 40
- On the Warpath 42
- The Journey East 44

ACT III – THE SIEGE OF EXCELSIS 51
- Distant Thunder 52
- The Oncoming Horde 56
- The Seven Towers Besieged . . . 58
- The Shattering Blow 60
- The Voice and the Talon 62
- To Strike Like Lightning 64
- Gods and Monsters 66
- The City's Dark Heart 68

GODS AND CHAMPIONS 76

THE RULES 85

BROKEN REALMS 86
- Campaign Rules 87
- Realm of Battle: The Coast of Tusks, Ghur 88
- Streets of Death 89
- Battleplan: The Rite of Life . . . 90
- Battleplan: They Came From Below 92
- Battleplan: Clash of Giants . . . 94
- Battleplan: Last Flight of the Scarlet Scourge 96
- Battleplan: Dark Heart 98
- Battleplan: Of Gods and Monsters 100

BATTLETOME UPDATES 103

DESTRUCTION 106
- Kragnos, the End of Empires . 106

GLOOMSPITE GITZ 108
- Bad Moon Loonshrine 108
- Jaws of Mork Allegiance Abilities 110
- Moon-jumper Stampede 111
- Moon-biter Squigalanche . . . 111
- Glogg's Megamob Allegiance Abilities 112
- Stomping Megamob 113
- Grimscuttle Tribes Allegiance Abilities 114
- Grimscuttle Spider Cluster . . 115
- Grimscuttle Skitterswarm . . . 115
- Grimscuttle Nest 115

SYLVANETH 116
- Alarielle the Everqueen 116
- Warsong Revenant 117
- Awakened Wyldwood 118
- Drycha's Spitegrove 119

HEDONITES OF SLAANESH 120
- Dexcessa, the Talon of Slaanesh 120
- Synessa, the Voice of Slaanesh 122
- The Exquisite Pursuit 123

CITIES OF SIGMAR 124
- Free City of Excelsis 124
- Doralia ven Denst 126
- Galen ven Denst 127

SERAPHON 128
- Lord Kroak 128

SKAVEN 130
- The Skaventide Battle Traits . 130
- Clans Moulder Mutations . . . 130
- Rattachak's Doom-coven 132

BEASTS OF CHAOS 133
- The Butcher-herd 133
- Warpaths of the Beastherds Battle Traits 134
- Beastlord 135
- Jabberslythe 135

PITCHED BATTLE PROFILES 136

PRODUCED BY THE WARHAMMER STUDIO

With thanks to The Faithful for their additional playtesting services

British Cataloguing-in-Publication Data. A catalogue record for this book is available from the British Library. Pictures used for illustrative purposes only.

Games Workshop Ltd., Willow Road, Lenton, Nottingham, NG7 2WS, United Kingdom

games-workshop.com

DRAMATIS PERSONAE

As the Soul Wars faded and a new era of war began, many forces converged upon the Ghurish Heartlands. They were a crux point in the new order, and the forces that battled to control them were titanic in scale and multifarious in number. The gods themselves struggled to wrest the course of history to their advantage.

GODS OF THE MORTAL REALMS

- **Kragnos, the End of Empires:** The Living Earthquake. God of seismic destruction from the fallen land of Donse. Eternal enemy of the slann and their draconic allies.

- **Alarielle the Everqueen:** Resurgent ruler of Ghyran; monarch of the Sylvaneth; bane of dark forces across the Jade Kingdoms; goddess of life, renewal and the seasons. Sworn enemy of Nurgle.

- **Morathi-Khaine and the Shadow Queen:** Two incarnations of the same soul. Goddess of shade, murder and duplicity. A traitor to the throne of Sigmar Heldenhammer.

- **Sigmar Heldenhammer:** The God-King; the Hammer of the Heavens; Master of High Azyr; Father of the Stormhosts; the Last Unberogen; deity of thunder, war and strength in adversity.

FORCES OF DESTRUCTION

- **Gordrakk, the Fist of Gork:** Greatest of all orruk warlords, Ironjaw Megaboss and rider of the savage Maw-krusha known as Bigteef.

- **Skragrott the Loonking:** High ruler of the Moonclan Grots, boss of Skrappa Spill and chosen of the Bad Moon.

- **Gulgaz Stoneklaw:** Warboss of the Bonesplitterz of the Flamescar Plateau. Making a pilgrimage to Ghur under the instruction of the shrunken heads of his former advisors.

- **Glogg:** Dankhold Troggoth and unwitting troggherd leader whose rampage across the Spiral Crux has taken him through a realmgate to the hunting grounds of Ghur.

- **Derko Walrusbiter:** Irascible Kraken-eater of the Gallet Stomp. Known to be the brains of the operation, but given the intelligence of his fellow Mega-Gargants, that's not saying much.

CHAMPIONS OF ORDER

- **Drycha Hamadreth:** Bitter and misanthropic leader of the Dreadwood. Cares only for the Sylvaneth and wishes painful death upon all other races.

- **Galen and Doralia ven Denst:** Spell hunters and witchbane agents specialising in the demise of corrupted mages and their works. Members of the Order of Azyr.

- **Cerrus Sentanus, the White Reaper, Lord-Veritant of the Knights Excelsior:** Leader of the Consecralium's resistance against the Chaos threat in Excelsis. Widely held to be the most terrifying individual in the entire city.

- **Meloria Evenblade, Lord-Castellant of the Knights Excelsior:** Defender of the City of Secrets and mistress of the seven towers.

- **Lord Kroak:** Legendary slann who sits beyond death, ancient and mummified in corporeal form but shining and resplendent in spiritual potency.

- **Odo Maulgen:** Leader of the Nullstone Brotherhood and fanatical opponent of the arcane in all its forms.

AGENTS OF CHAOS

- **Synessa, the Voice of Slaanesh:** The risen godspawn of Slaanesh – Chaos god of excess, obsession and debauchery – whose voice compels the soul to dark deeds.

- **Dexcessa, the Talon of Slaanesh:** The second of the two majestic avatars of the Dark Prince born of Morathi's ascension to godhood. Loves the thrill of battle above all.

- **Ghorraghan Khai:** Savage Bray-Shaman of the Ghyranite Butcher-herd, who walk as men but wish nothing but violence upon all of civilisation.

- **Rattachak:** Warlock Bombardier of the Clans Skryre, self-proclaimed demolitions expert and prodigy in the art of blaming others for disasters great and small.

THE RITE OF LIFE

The defeat of Nagash in distant Hysh had sent ripples of causality across the realms. In Ghyran, the Everqueen Alarielle was poised to capitalise on this with a grand resurgence, triggering a cascade of consequences both glorious and dire.

She sang as she killed, her throat stinging with the slow-burning power of the melody. She could feel a tingling on the soles of her bare feet as the Oak of Ages Past thrummed with power beneath her. The colossal fallen tree, one of two legendary remnants of the World Before Time, lay half-submerged in the dank quagmire of Rotwater Blight. Here she would weave a new beginning. Here she would bring to bear the midsummer height of her power, not only to make a statement but to turn the course of history.

If she could survive.

Splashing through the stinking, knee-deep swampland of the Blight were mould-skinned beastmen, their untidy manes matted into slabs that bounced on their shoulders as they ran. Eyes rolling wildly, their voices were raised in a cacophony, the bleating and screaming like the din of a hundred abattoirs. Towering, bull-headed monstrosities waded through their ranks, those few healthy plants that had fought their way to survival in the tainted waters withering at the sheer evil of their aura as they passed. Each brandished savage hacking blades or had limbs that ended in axes, hatchets and cleavers just as suited to felling trees as bisecting their prey with each sweep. They stared at Alarielle with the purest hatred, driven into a raging frenzy by the purity of her song. Carried by four hulking Ghorgons was the Dirgehorn, that Nurgle-fouled Ghyranite artefact torn from the skull of a godbeast to sound the death of nations. It had been shattered over a century ago by the silver Stormhost of the Hallowed Knights, yet in their wake, its fragments had been painstakingly gathered, pressed together then regrown with foul Nurglite blessings. Here that relic was again, held together with sutures of bulging, cankerous flesh to give full voice to its mind-shredding bellow.

Around Alarielle, a ring of Treelords raised their voices to bolster her song of life; the ominous bass notes of elder oaks groaning in the storm formed a rich counterpoint for her swelling, swirling contralto. Ringed around them were thousands of Sylvaneth, sprouted in the space of a few short hours and spreading out amidst the brackish water like a forest. Amongst them were Drycha Hamadreth and her fellows from the Dreadwood, a cloud of angry spites buzzing and biting around them as, hissing and thrashing, they vented their rage on the bestial intruders. Over the course of the night, the Sylvaneth had fought hard to reach the Oak, and many hundreds of the forest spirits had fallen to the giant slug-like daemons that belly-flopped from the muck to bar their path. Now, with the dawn light filtering through the miasmas of the marsh, the massed circles of the Sylvaneth position were complete, forming something like the rings of a tree, with the genesis of them all – Alarielle – at their heart. Their success came not a minute too soon, for the twisted forests at the edge of the Blight shivered with the power of the brutish beastmen forcing their way through them.

Louder grew the spirit-song, screams caught and intertwined with the melody as Alarielle's contralto swooped and soared. They only made the music stronger. The darting of her fingertips wove the thick forest around her into spears of hardwood that punched through the chests and throats of the braying monsters closing in. The sacrifice of a living, sentient creature – that was the most potent of ingredients, even for a spell cast by a god.

The sap-like blood of dying Sylvaneth mingled with the dark discolourations leaking from the beastman corpses. It swirled in the waters at the blackened, fossilised roots of the Oak of Ages Past, swilling in hypnotic patterns through the quagmire that once ran clear as the River Vitalis but now was known as the Gelid Gush. Where it touched the bark of that grand fallen tree, it disappeared as if drunk by a thirsting man.

Sensing imminence in the air, the larger beastmen – snorting, flesh-craving brutes each broad enough to wrestle a Treelord – redoubled their assault. They smashed through the Sylvaneth at the defensive formation's rim like a battering ram driven into a thin palisade wall. Alarielle's eye twitched at the sight, but she faltered not at all.

The song rose higher and stronger, the strains of its melody near visible as shimmers of jade energy in the air. To Alarielle's profound relief, the Oak of Ages Past shivered and pulsed in time under her feet. Its roots twitched and quested, seeking out fallen Sylvaneth; as they gave themselves to it, melding voluntarily with its ancient wood, the Oak grew more vital.

Storming toward Alarielle came a wedge of braying, four-armed giants, their sheer size making the Bray-Shaman that led them look small by comparison. He made up for it by turning to dust every Dryad and Tree-Revenant that dared block his path, for his skull-topped stave crackled with dark energies that could kill with a touch. A shock assault, blunt and direct. It was exactly what she had come to expect from the idiot beastmen. They had been driven into a frenzy of hatred by the purity of her song and higher thought was lost to them.

She had been counting on it, in fact.

Their fury gave them a terrible strength. More and more of the forest people were cut down. Even though it needed to happen, Alarielle felt every death as a wound deep in her breast. These were her children, and she would mourn them all, in time. Their names would be woven into songs of remembrance, for their lamentirii would not be recovered; they would neither be replanted nor grow anew. The spirit-song had a greater use for them.

Under her feet, the Oak began to move, nourished by the souls of the departed. Climbing down to the lower roots, she circled the Spear of Kurnoth in the water, and there the River Vitalis ran clear once more, swirling around and around to form a whirlpool of jade energies that banished the stain of Nurgle's corruption. The Oak's roots, each the thickness of an elder tree in its own right, dived deep into the river bed and grew taut. They too were limbs, of a sort, and as they shivered and shuddered to the music of the spirit-song, they were hauling the Oak's fallen immensity slowly upright. The ancient, dead wood of the tree, petrified during its aetheric drift from the world of its birth to the realmsphere of Ghyran, was turning from black to brown and, in places, putting forth tiny buds of green.

In the middle distance, Drycha Hamadreth and her fellow Dreadwood spirits were whipping, impaling and crushing the life from the beastmen that escorted the Dirgehorn. What had started as a swift, well-coordinated strike launched from beneath the waters had turned into a gruesome massacre grinding back and forth in the muck. Before the battle, Drycha had promised to break the back of them with the hurricane force of her assault, but she had yet to fulfil her promise – protecting their sacred artefact, the beasts would not yield. The grey-green miasma around them was tinged with a pink mist, and the pungent smell of spilt bloodsap and spattering gore mingled thickly enough that Alarielle could scent it half a mile away. Then, as a pair of black-barked Treelords swept their colossal blades over the heads of the thick-pressed beastmen and into the limbs of the Ghorgons behind, two of the Dirgehorn's bearers toppled, and the great, booming artefact fell into the blood-tinged mire.

The sudden absence of that fell noise was like blissful, healing water bathing the mind. Shorn of competition, Alarielle's song rose to a soaring crescendo, her Spirits of Durthu shaking leaf and bough as they poured centuries of anguish and fiery rebellion into their own chorus. Above them, the Oak of Ages Past rose higher, hauling itself upright to blossom into wondrous, unstoppable life. Leaves by the thousand sprouted from fossilised driftwood, buds opened into white flowers haloed by pollen, and glowing acorns of gold swelled to fruition before falling to land in the clear waters of the whirlpool still rushing around the revenant tree's roots.

Wherever they landed, a nest of tendrils and stalks grew with rushing, sudden speed as Alarielle poured her magic into the soil of Ghyran. There was no shadow of death upon the land since Nagash's spell had been broken, and the curse of Nurgle, though lingering, was waning as her own waxed strong. Here, under her auspice, Ghyran remembered what it once was, and it grew mighty. The cycle of rebirth was the most sacred of all, and death was not the end.

The gold-tinged acorns that had fallen into the swirling waters grew larger, before splitting to reveal foetal forms. Uncurling under Alarielle's triumphant gaze, they turned from green-limbed infants to slender youths to tall, broad-shouldered revenants born from another time, another legend. Up they stood, strange and beautiful all at once, creatures seeded from the World-that-Was and grown to maturity in a matter of minutes within the fecund bosom of Ghyran. They opened mouths sticky with sap, pulled forth long splinters of oak from within their gullets, and as one, they shaped and elongated the wooden spars into long flutes. Sharing a glance, they put their mouths to the fife-like instruments and began to play.

To Alarielle, the sound they produced was as swirls of rich honey added to the intoxicating mead of her song; it was so sweet and uplifting that it made tears of maternal pride course down her cheeks. To the beastmen, it was a sonic assault of devastating potency. Copiously bleeding eardrums painted the sides of shaggy heads crimson with gore. Those enemies close by spasmed and shook as if in a terrible fever, eyeballs bursting and fat tongues lolling down to their chests as if they had been hanged. As the skirling melodies harmonised with the spirit-song, the land itself came to life, new and vital foliage pushing through the swampy muck to reach towards the skies. Fortified by the pipers' music, the forest of pale green tendrils wound like dancing serpents then lashed out at the mutated creatures still fighting to crush the Sylvaneth battleline. Hardwood points punched into bestial flesh, sprouting new shoots into the veins and arteries of their victims until they were bursting with vegetative life. Strong, curling vines wrapped around wattled throats, squeezing and choking, the bulge-eyed beastmen turning crimson-faced as the air was crushed out of them. A hundred horrific sights expanded out across the marshlands, each nonetheless pleasing to Alarielle's eyes.

Rippling waves of vegetation sprouted from the wetlands, the Nurgle-tainted water running clean once more as the pure energies of Ghyran overcame the curse that had blighted them for so long. The tipping point had been reached. No longer fighting entropy and death at the same time, the irresistible swell of nature was healing that which had so long been accursed. The magic of the Oak of Ages Past added its aeons-old power to the swell of life, and to Alarielle's fierce jubilation, the wetlands became a landscape of burgeoning seedlings, then a swathe of saplings, then a young and vital woodland stretching far into the distance. There was a scent to it that brought back a rush of memory, a fragment of Alarielle's former life reborn. A name sprung to the forefront of her mind and, with it, a bittersweet surge of emotion:

Athel Loren.

The spirit-song's music had reached a crescendo, and as the impossibly tall Oak rose to become fully vertical, Alarielle summoned her Wardroth steed to her with a pulse of thought. From a swirl of glowing motes akin to a swarm of fireflies, the gigantic insectoid sprite coalesced, its broad carapace forming beneath her feet as she stepped from the Oak's golden-brown bark onto the curve of the beetle's back. It was warm to the touch, its spirit close to the surface. Already she could feel its repulsion at the bestial creatures still howling for blood around it twinned with a desire to trample, gouge and impale those who offended its mistress.

Ghorraghan Khai, shaman of the herd, had hewn a wide path towards her. Even as she watched, the creature ducked a crushing swing from the young Treelord Therenduain and thrust its staff into an open bole-wound; a moment later, the mighty Sylvaneth shuddered and rotted away to dust. No normal strength behind the blow, then, but the tainted magic of one favoured by the Dark Gods. And still it was as nothing to the slow, certain power of nature.

Alarielle curled the strange, branch-like claw of her left hand and the shaman was suddenly entwined by thorny vines, each the thickness of a man's arm. Tossing its horn-crowned head, it ripped through a great many of them, tearing its own flesh to ribbons in the process. On the beastman came, bellowing its intent to drink her blood in its foul tongue.

She raised an eyebrow, just a little, and tapped her toe on the Wardroth's back. The monstrous spite charged, dipping its three-horned head before impaling the shaman through the chest with one massive, razored antler. It barrelled onwards, spiking and gouging at the monstrous Ghorgons that came on behind their leader. Alarielle dealt with those it did not smash into the dirt, swaying aside from their blows whilst tearing out throats and hearts – each like a pulsing red boulder – with the Spear of Kurnoth. Still impaled, the beastman shaman battered her Wardroth's iron-hard carapace, its fearsome anger sustaining it even with such a grievous wound. Yet here its magic held no sway.

When Alarielle turned her blazing eyes upon it, the creature writhed free of the giant horn's prong and disappeared into the River Vitalis with a bleating scream.

Welcome, my children. She did not speak it aloud but sent a pulse of thought to each of the revenant pipers that had sprung into being at the union of the Oak and the newly cleansed waters of the River Vitalis. The pipers inclined their heads as one in recognition, playing their music all the while. *One day, we will rest and bask in what we have made for the sake of all. For now, go, and take my song with you.*

The neonatal Sylvaneth, each exuding the confidence of an elder spirit, rose up into the air on thermals of sheer magic. Great arcs of living matter grew like crests above their shoulders to frame them against the troubled Ghyranite skies. Their piping grew louder, each reinforcing the same melody – a new strain full of hope, a dawning and a promise. As they moved out into the landscape, the lands blossomed and flourished around them.

It was not peaceful life that grew so swiftly around them, nor was it beautiful to any other than the Sylvaneth. Rather, it was that part of nature that sought to reclaim, to enwrap, to take for its own. What had previously been a swathe of wetlands had become a forest, and the plants within it were now warriors. The land itself came to life, green shoots twisting as they grew to push into the flesh of the beastmen all around, tearing it asunder. The Dirgehorn was caught up, carried high on a nest of tendrils and, with a great crack of tearing keratin, split once more in twain.

Outwards went the bow wave of Ghyranite magic as Alarielle's rite reached its climax. She shuddered with relief, her leaf-wings bearing her upwards as the Wardroth charged down those few foes still somehow clinging to life. Up she drifted, the bleating of dying beastmen fading as she passed the boughs of the Oak of Ages and reached the dizzying heights of its new, flourishing canopy. The great spell of renewal would cascade across Ghyran, and, as its unstoppable melody was carried by the Warsong Revenants into the other realms, the lands themselves would be galvanised to fight back against the Dark Gods. It was a new beginning, and it would set in motion a chain of events that even she did not truly fathom.

Yet to replace the cloying curse of death with the boon of vital new life, it was surely worth the cost.

The life magic spread onwards like the creepers of a rose,
The tendrils of a thirsting plant, questing for new soil,
Borne by the revenants the Everqueen had summoned
From the Oak of Ages Past.

The spirit-song was carried far across Ghyran,
Spread from portal and gate into the other realms.
On it went, its irresistible melody
Caught in the minds of those it touched.

To the lesser creatures of the worlds, it was nourishment,
To the wounded in body and mind, blessed relief.
To the creatures of Chaos, it was torment:
They heard only the screaming wrath of the lands.

Weapon and balm all at once was the song,
Blessing and curse alike.
The weft and weave of fate remade.
Where once was stagnation, now came a surge.

In once-fair Ghyran, the plants grew fierce,
Tearing at the flesh of the unnatural and vile.
The light of Hysh took solarite forms.
Even grave-cold Shyish found the touch of life upon it.

Fierce Aqshy saw a thousand fires walk the land.
In mercurial Chamon, strange tides moulded
silver and gold.
Eyes opened amidst Ulgu's mists, sinister and cruel.
In Azyr, living lightning struck and did not fade.

Yet it was Ghur that shivered most to the strain.
Its bestial landscapes, so close to sentience already,
Spawned new and raging life
Whilst yielding that which had long slumbered.

The mountains shuddered and split,
And the land split with them.
From deep within those peaks, an ancient prison broke
And a primal god came forth.

Long ago, there was a lord of Donse.
He whose hoofbeats split the lands.
He who made the Dread Mace,
Its haft hewn of Ghur's bones.

His shield Tuskbreaker torn from the earth
Where Gorkamorka,
Finding it not good to eat,
Had hurled it in his anger.

Nothing could stop him then.
He and his kin broke the land.
Two-legs hunted by Four;
Legends fell to his mace.

Then came the scaled drakes,
Sun-hatched, Ghur-blessed.
In seeking to fell him,
They made an eternal foe.

He climbed their mountains.
He trampled their nests.
He split open their cities.
He gorged on their young.

The land broke under his hooves.
The drake-lord cities fell,
Consumed by Kragnos' rage,
Eaten by Ghur's endless maw.

Their vengeance was long in coming:
Cold-bloods feel not the fire of temper.
Lizard, drake and god-serpent
Worked a great spell upon him.

Trapped in the mountain was Kragnos,
Caught in a prison of time.
He raged but could not break it.
He roared but was not heard.

There he waits for his moment,
His people long gone to dust.
Yet when the land splits once more,
He will break free to rise again.

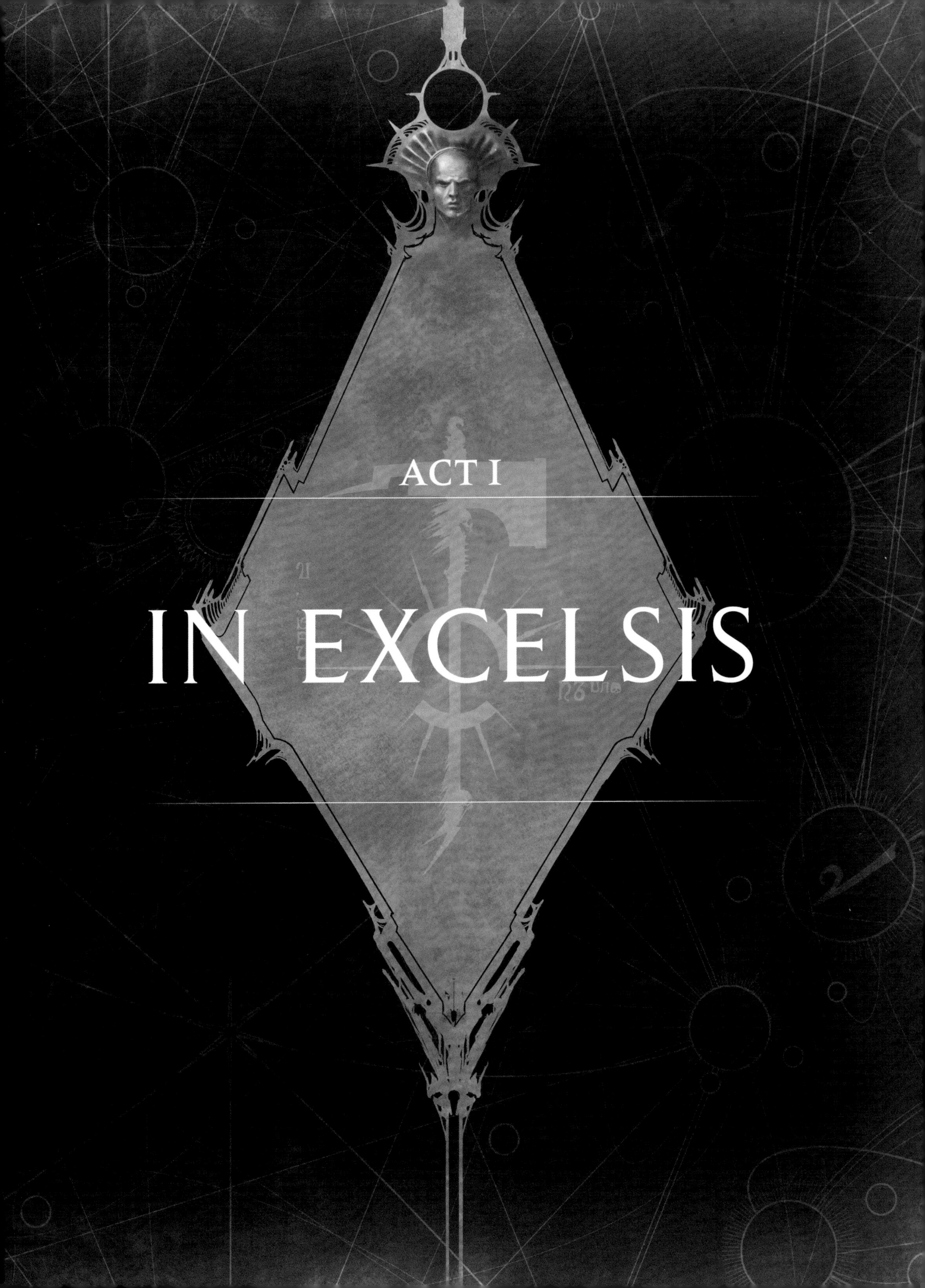

ACT I

IN EXCELSIS

BESTIAL WILDERNESS

The rugged, primeval landscapes of the Realm of Beasts obey one law alone: kill or be killed. Here the very land is alive – or so it is said by the shamans and elders of the tribes that have found a way to survive in this realm.

In Ghur, each crevasse and fissure is like unto a rocky maw that can grind shut on the unwary and feast on their remains; each tree seeks to poison or impale so as to grow strong on the corpses of the fallen; and thousands upon thousands of species seek to prey upon one another before they are devoured in turn. Even the landmasses are locked in a slow, tectonic hunt, grinding over one another so that the mighty can eclipse the weak. Such was the fate of Donse, the former home of the Drogrukh race, from which the deity of earthquakes, Kragnos, originally hailed. It has been all but consumed by the geological shift of Thondia, the continent whose edge harbours the Coast of Tusks. There lies the Sigmarite capital of Excelsis, a city that is very much on the edge of catastrophe.

CARCASS DONSE
Once as mighty a continent as Thondia, this fallen land contains only fossilised remnants of its former grandeur.

TWINHORN PEAK
This massive mountain characterised by soaring, horn-like double peaks was the prison of Kragnos for many an age.

GHURISH HEARTLANDS
EXCELSIS, CITY OF SECRETS
This sprawling port-city mines the nearby Spear of Mallus for magical, prophetic stone.
Mangrel Isle
The Ravenids
The Drench
Thunderscorn Peaks
Vensoth Bay
The Great Gutfort
Izalend
Icefangs
Clawing Sea
Thondia
Great Excelsis Road
The Stamping
Meatfist Mawpath
Krondspine Range
Coast of Tusks
The Mar
Bilgeport
Lake Everglut
Ursricht's Kill
Glossom Crevasse
Spear of Mallus
Excelsis
Vexothskol
Krondskol
Breakface Mawpath
The Gnarlwood
Morruk Hills
Questing Serpent River
Stone Nautilor
Ymnog's Trample (North)
Fraktoa Crevasse
Lost Mesas
Bloodgullet Mawpath
Nautil Peaks
Carcass Donse
Templia Beasthall
Gallet
River Slannstongue
Koatl's Gullet
Primeval Jungle
Crawling Pits of Gharrentia
Mekitopsar
Holdbrawl Mawpath
Plains of Mekitopsar
Brokenjarl Mawpath
Greatpeaks of Andtor
Underchasm Gulch
Godswallow Delta
Lake Hoarfrost
Ravening Rivers
Mouldberpit
Fasting Veldt
Sea
Andtor
Bantu's Gate
Rimelake
The Gnawing Fords
Everwinter's Claim
Icebrow
Bjarl Throat
Shatterland Floes
Krakensea
Greedmouth
Harassic Cliffs
Ramhut's Spine
Ymnog's Trample (South)
Colossal Bite
Bjarl
Lookaway Point
Ruins of Ventivia
Corpse Lakes
Deffgorge
War of Basilisks
Wake of Fangathrak
Fangsgirdle
Drakbiter Mawpath
The Ivory Citadel
Lake Maw
Ur-Luparl's Shellpeaks
Ghurish Necrosia

BRINK OF DESTRUCTION

Excelsis once thrived as one of Sigmar's prized capital fortress-cities, but since the coming of the Arcanum Optimar, it has weathered invasion from within and without. Only now, as a surge of life spreads across Thondia, is it becoming clear just how deep the corruptions of Chaos run.

Excelsis is known as the City of Secrets – and for good reason. Its citizenry gave it the name owing to the prophetic ore mined there, and the glimpses of future events acquired from this material have kept the city alive despite its location in the primal wilderness of the Ghurish Heartlands. Recently, the name has taken on a more unsettling resonance, for the powers of disorder seek to tip Excelsis into total disaster.

The city of Excelsis is built around a bay on the Coast of Tusks that harbours the colossal Spear of Mallus. A pillar of sigmarite somewhat like a vast stalactite that has dropped from the heavens and impaled the sea bed, the Spear is a sacred religious relic to the Devoted of the God-King and a source of limitless opportunity to everyone else. Every day, flinders of the Spear are chipped away by the metalith-borne miners that hover around it, then to be traded as 'glimmerings'. Each glimmering is more valuable than gold. To hold even a pebble-sized amount in one's hand is to tap into the celestial energy within it. A tiny shard will give but a single, often trivial image in the mind's eye, whereas a fist-sized chunk will yield many visions of futures yet to come. By interpreting these prophecies and acting upon them before they come to pass, such scryers can ensure they are best placed to capitalise on them. So it is that the fisher-guilds of Excelsis take massive hauls from the ocean without falling prey to its many sea monsters, the rulers of the city send their armies to Thondia's realmgates when they are sure the chances of success are most favourable, and the schemers and politicians of the city are embroiled in a never-ending battle of intrigue. Unfortunately, prophecy is far from a precise science. All of the foresight available to Excelsis did not prevent the city's invasion by the forces of Tzeentch. In fact, it more than likely it caused it, for the Changer of the Ways has always been drawn to the arcane.

It was Ortam Vermyre, High Arbiter and well-regarded member of the city's elite, who precipitated Excelsis's darkest hour. As a leading member of the Cult of the Fated Path, he ensured that he and his fellows infiltrated every stratum of the city from common scribe to vaunted aristocrat – he even had agents in the Collegiate Arcane who ensured that any prophecy concerning his duplicity was snuffed out or misinterpreted. Though Stormcast Eternals

marched through the streets each day on their way to war with the greenskins of Thondia, they did not learn the scale of the cult's activity within the city until it was almost too late. Were it not for the intervention of a common Freeguild sergeant, Armand Callis, and the witch hunter Hanniver Toll, the secret plot to raze Excelsis would have come to fruition all but unopposed.

Since the uprising of the Tzeentchian cults and their subsequent defeat, the protectors of the Sigmarite metropolis have turned their gaze inwards. The Knights Excelsior worked tirelessly to quarantine the corrupted areas of the city that could not be cleansed and excise the rest. Unfortunately, word spread far and wide that Excelsis had suffered a major onslaught. Like sharks to blood in the water, the savage and the monstrous were closing in on the city with a killing light in their eyes, even as another Chaos power was seeding a strange worship of its own…

TUMULT ARCANA

In Ghur, to stay in one place is to court disaster. Each wall built in that realm will ultimately be knocked down. Despite this widely acknowledged truth, Excelsis has become a powerful presence in the Ghurish Heartlands, which, in turn, has given rise to powerful enemies.

The streets of Excelsis were still scarred by the calamitous invasions of Ortam Vermyre's uprising. Those areas quarantined over a decade ago by the Knights Excelsior were left well alone on pain of death, but every so often, an arcane emanation would burn through the streets from that unhallowed ground – an echo of the sorcery that nearly caused the city's downfall.

It was the Order of Azyr that was tasked with taking down such spectral emanations, for in their role as hunters of the eldritch, they were perhaps the only citizens outside of the Stormcast Sacrosanct chambers who were capable of such a feat. They were led by the veteran witch hunter Galen ven Denst – a scion of the Amethyst Princedoms and distant relative of Eonid ven Denst himself, known since his Reforging as Ionus Cryptborn – and his daughter Doralia. A prodigy in the persecution of the unnatural arts with a marksman's eye, Doralia had perfected the art of etching crossbow bolts with tiny runes of banishment, an aspect of runecraft she and her father had learnt in their sojourn to the Hyshian city of Settler's Gain. On more than one occasion, she had, from her sniper's eyrie high in the Consecral Bells, shot the spherical form of a rogue spell with such a bolt, striking the emanation's very centre and unbinding the magic that held it together. Her father employed much the same technique with the silver stakes he used as his own weapons of choice; when driven into the heart, they could discorporate a night-gheist or slay a vampire in a single, screaming second. However, even these members of the Order were only human, and they could not be everywhere at once.

The mood amongst the citizenry was turning ugly. They were a superstitious people, many of whom were Ghurish natives who had entered the city as Reclaimed, and most of them had but a few phials of Aqua Ghyranis – the healing water that was the common currency of the Cities of Sigmar. They made their hovels and shanty towns out of hides, bones and monstrous teeth taken from the corpses of beached sea monsters; their lives were pragmatic and short, and they had little truck with magic. Anywhere they saw the spoor of the arcane, they clucked their tongues and made the sign of the twin-tailed comet. They were not alone; many amongst the city's monied echelons, having lost their holdings during the invasion, wanted nothing to do with magic of any kind. After all, it had been sorcery that had brought them to their current predicament.

The backlash against magical artifice was embodied by the Nullstone Brotherhood, a citizen-led Sigmarite orthodoxy of the Devoted creed that worked hand in glove with the Order of Azyr. Thought by some to be a network of bruisers, busybodies and informants, it had nonetheless proven extremely useful in weeding out the last of the Tzeentchian cultists and hidden mutants who had ushered in the invasion. More than that, it was actively pursuing the rumours that bipedal rat-men stalked the tunnels under the city. The leaders had nailed more than one of the creatures to the front doors of their temples as proof that the skaven were active inside the city walls, though their corpses would almost always vanish in the night.

The Nullstone Brotherhood never rested, operating day and night to sniff out those who would associate with Chaos; most of its faithful wore only sackcloth and hide, shaved their scalps close and bore tattoos of hammers and comets across their faces and necks. They were so intimidating in appearance and manner that few gainsaid them, and with each mutant they burned at the stake, with each verminous skaven they dragged screeching from the sewers, their creed gathered more sway.

As the sense of unease and omens of destruction grew ever more potent, the Brotherhood's unwavering puritanism saw them turn their attentions from those magic users who worshipped Chaos to any who used the eldritch arts in any way. Saints of a sort rose through the ranks, foremost amongst them Odo Maulgen, a seven-foot warrior priest from the barbarian tribes of Lendu so naturally hirsute he had to shave his head three times a day to maintain his priestly appearance.

Maulgen had a particular hatred for the city's aelves. His former tribe had been raided by what he believed were aelves of the sea, and he had long sought a way to get even. He and his followers began to hunt aelven practitioners of magic above all others, their sermons conflating the idea of magic use and aelven heritage as one and the same. Wealth, privilege and

narcissism too were seen as signs of those who were involved with the arcane. Mirrors were deemed unnatural gateways to the daemonic and were confiscated en masse by his salvation corps. Bigotry and prejudice against the aelves thrived, with the city's ills being blamed on scapegoats whose aloof manner made them easy targets. Unfortunately, with so many citizens already in the sway of the Nullstone Brotherhood, those views became widespread, and the city began to turn on itself.

Over time, more and more aelves disappeared from the streets. At first, this was seen as nothing unusual, for aelves came and went as they pleased, and though their leaders theoretically answered to the city's Grand Conclave, in practice, they had a vast degree of autonomy. After all, the most part of the city's famous naval presence was aelven, and the Scourge Privateers were a common sight in the city docks. Yet there were rumours of aelves being stolen from the streets, hessian sacks over their heads and garrottes around their throats, never to return. Tensions simmered, for many captains of the Excelsis armada were not the sort to sit idly by as their kin were abducted on the flimsiest of pretexts. Acts of sudden and sadistic retribution, up to and including the flaying of members of the Brotherhood who had been seen near aelven abduction sites, made the spectre of civil war ever starker. The city slid towards its own destruction, and none were any the wiser as to the true reasons behind it all.

There had been many a disturbing prophecy circulated in the city's upper echelons, glimpsed by those with enough wealth and influence to purchase large quantities of glimmerings harvested from the Spear of Mallus. Some saw brown rivers of verminous filth pouring through the streets; others saw giant green feet trampling on a child's wooden township or a plague of serpents vomited out from the sea. More still detailed vast, scale-covered wyrms constricting around glittering sceptres or suturing chasms shut with fangs that reflected sacred starlight. So many portents of doom were passed through the populace that the people of Excelsis became numb to them. After an initial wave of panic and trepidation, they began seeing the omens of disaster more as entertainment than as any particular call to action; gallows humour was much in evidence, and in the gambling dens of the dockyards, they even placed bets on which they thought would come true and thereby claim the city's downfall first. Through it all, the citizenry in general went about their business, each feeling in their hearts the cloud of disaster looming above them but unwilling or unable to do anything about it.

TENSIONS RUN HIGH

The City of Secrets was abuzz with rumours about the shadows looming over it, for its stock in trade was prophecy and the omens were dark indeed. Only a few brave souls could see past their own prejudice and self-interest to comprehend the true scale of the disasters to come – and, in doing so, fight to avert them.

The atmosphere of threat thickened in the city streets and, in response, the acts of the agitated citizenry grew bolder. Wherever soothsayers or bone-scryers had set up shop, they were dragged from their hide-covered yurts and forcibly exiled into the Thondian wilderness at the point of a spear. Every human clique had something to say about every other; every shanty blamed its neighbours for the roving spells that the Order of Azyr fought so hard to put down. The duardin of the Forgequarter Sprawl remained largely out of things, for it was well known that they did not cast spells and instead trusted in only the most stable forms of magic. Besides, those who picked a fight with a duardin soon found their reputation for legendary constitution and stubbornness to be well earned.

It was the aelves of Excelsis who took the brunt of the rising discontent. Privateers, Wanderers and ambassadorial Lumineth found themselves treated with open hostility and even violence. In the overcrowded merchant districts known as the Teemings, scuffles broke out as those who saw themselves as beyond reproach booed and attacked isolated groups of aelves regardless of affiliation, pelting them with rotten fruit and nightsoil or even stoning them alive when they were unable to slip away. Many of these indignities were paid for in blood, with slender aelven blades opening holes in the ranks of the hollering mobs as a manner of escape. In killing their persecutors, they only made martyrs of them. Agitators and demagogues stoked the flames, and so the situation grew worse.

As word spread after each killing, each new death led to more and more citizens falling under the Brotherhood's sway. Maulgen had boosted his own credentials by claiming to be working directly for the White Reaper of the Consecralium, a figure of fear in the city owing to the merciless potency of his purges. Given Maulgen's imposing stature and steely charisma, none had the spine to gainsay him, especially given that there were already rumours that any insurrections in his camp had been put down by a sustained beating more than once. In their haste to prove their antagonism towards magic and the wealth that could afford it, his followers gave away their worldly belongings and wore only sackcloth, even going so far as to wear hair shirts and other trappings of punishment to display their humility and virtue.

Others paid for oaths of vengeance to be tattooed across their bodies from head to toe or purchased nullstone amulets that they wore with pride over their clothes, knowing that, in that anti-theurgic mineral, they had a measure of protection from hostile magic. Some, under the supervision of Odo Maulgen, hammered chunks of nullstone directly into their flesh and bound them there with twine, a mockery of the Fyreslayer practice of melding ur-gold runes with their musculature to honour their fiery deity Grimnir. These latter kindred were known as Nullers, and there was never a shortage of them to volunteer when the Brotherhood decided it was time to hunt down a witchmaid or burn an aelven warlock at the stake.

From the safety of the Palace Excelsium, the Grand Conclave proposed a motion to disband the Nullstone Brotherhood. The city's Grand Matriarch, the battle-scarred ex-warrior Yarga-Sjuhan, had called an emergency muster after the disastrous Night of a Hundred Blindings. She told those assembled that six magic users had been burned alive in Punishment Square, and that they had died with such a spectacular burst of magic that those standing closest, having come to witness the execution, found their eyes melting in their sockets. Odo Maulgen attended the emergency meeting in person, and his contact in the Order of Azyr, Darrac Neve, stood with him. Only their impassioned speeches saved the Brotherhood from total dissolution. They agreed to keep the city in harmony by focusing their wrath solely on those whom the Grand Conclave deemed dangerously disruptive.

In secret, Maulgen and his fellows carried on abducting their aelven prey. Instead of capturing them, burning them in public and risking censure, however, they hustled them away to the disused ballroom that Maulgen had taken as his headquarters within the quarantined district known as the Crystalfall. Though the area was walled off from the rest of the city, and though trespassers were traditionally executed by the Knights Excelsior, it was still reachable by the sewer network if one knew which hidden passageways to traverse.

With the ballroom's shattered roof still letting in the rain, it was a cold and desolate place, but the symbolism of luxury brought low suited the Nullstone Brotherhood just fine. It was here that the Brotherhood kept the mirrors they had confiscated as a defence against the sin of vanity. Over six hundred mirrors of various shapes and sizes now lined its walls, ranging from lady's palm-mirrors to massive wall-sized reflectors taken from the mansions of Wellman's Row, and as many of them were broken as were intact. At Maulgen's insistence, the rope-bound aelves were slain in front of these mirrors instead of the populace, so that the last sight they ever saw would be the evidence of their own desperation and folly writ large upon their faces.

There was a great irony behind the weaponised intolerance of the Nullstone Brotherhood. In these ever-escalating acts of violence and persecution, Maulgen's faithful served not their ostensible patron Sigmar – who had become one with the magic of the heavens many millennia ago – but quite another power. In the end, all roads lead to acts of excess if travelled far enough, and Maulgen was not the only one to have a hall of mirrors as his sanctum. The die-hard followers of Odo Maulgen had become addicted to taking their creed to the most violent and sadistic extremes. And at the end of every form of extremism, waiting in the wings with a cruel smile on his blood-smeared lips, is the Dark Prince Slaanesh.

THE PROPHECIES OF EXCELSIS

Many of the Order of Azyr felt extremely uneasy about the citizenry taking it upon themselves to persecute magic users, but despite the constant petitioning from the Collegiate Arcane, there was no actual law against it. With Excelsis's finest prophets and soothsayers run out of the city, there were few left with experience enough to sort through the barrage of predictions – often contradictory – that were circulating through the streets. At first, Doralia ven Denst sought her answers by interrogating those she suspected of inflaming the city's conflicts, extracting rumours and gabbled truths at the tip of a crossbow bolt, but in consultation with her father Galen, she soon came to realise that the babblings of the terrified citizens she threatened were of limited use. She needed the advice of experts, not amateurs, of seers used to filtering the truth without bias – and of all the Order's allies, none were more objective than the Seraphon. It was this leap of logic that saw her and Galen seek out the Serpentanis, that strange, three-storey pyramid that served as the Seraphon embassy within the city's humid arboreal district.

Her weapons wrapped and stowed, Doralia made for the pictogram-covered pyramid with a confidence in her stride she did not feel. She could sense eyes on her and hear an occasional rustle in the trees that had nothing to do with the wind. Up the steps she ventured, passing spots of old blood and headless skeletons on the flagstones, until she vanished inside. Galen went to follow her but was somehow repelled; left gasping for air on the threshold, he watched his daughter disappear into the gloom.

THE VANISHING ARMADA

The presence of the Scourge Privateers in Excelsis was vital, for not only did they have a vast fleet of ships to call upon, they also had a way of corralling the sea monsters that lurked along the coastline, thereby forming an unusual but very effective barrier to any who would invade Excelsis by sea. They were as much a part of the city as the fisherfolk who fed it or the Stormcast Eternals who fought for it every day. They had stained their decks red time and time again whilst sailing along the Coast of Tusks, the Talon Coast and even the Mawbight. To aelves who had harpooned a leviathan or faced down a hunting ghyreshark, a tattered band of humans was no real threat. Small wonder, then, that those fools who assailed aelves on shore leave, thinking their numbers and nullstone amulets would tip the balance, were soon found amputated, flayed or even staked to the city walls as a warning to their fellows. The message was intended to be stark: leave the Scourge alone or suffer the same fate. Unfortunately, it merely added further fuel to the fires of strife and became a self-perpetuating cycle that led ever closer to civil war. It was the Nullstone Brotherhood that claimed victory in the end, however – one bright morning, the ships of the Scourge Privateers simply sailed away, leaving the harbour and coastal section of the city with only the thinnest of defences.

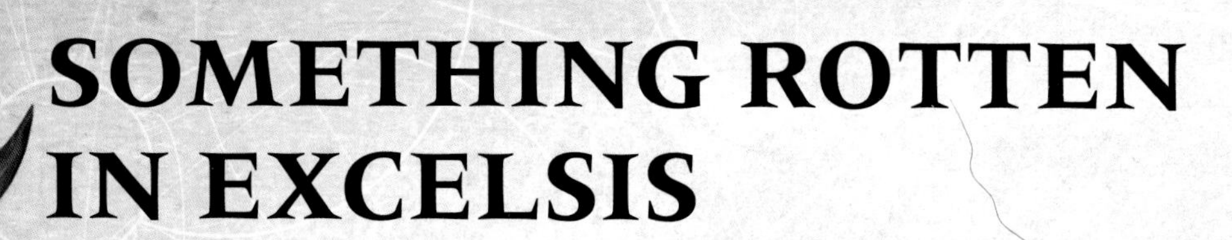

SOMETHING ROTTEN IN EXCELSIS

The doom that had cast its shadow over Excelsis unfurled itself. Those who would fight it each held part of the puzzle, but with so many enemies so close at hand, it would take a miracle for them to present a united front. Yet still, whilst good men and women took up their blades, there was a semblance of hope.

When Doralia left the Seraphon embassy, she did so with her back ramrod straight and her face bloodless. Outside the Serpentanis, Galen rushed to attend her; as her father, he knew instantly that something was wrong. The markswoman allowed herself to be guided to the Taverna District, drank three short glasses of imported fire-liquor in quick succession and shuddered out a long sigh before recounting her tale.

The dimensions inside the Serpentanis had little to do with those without. It was far, far larger than it had any right to be, and Doralia found herself breathing strange-tasting air as dragonflies and glimmer-winged insects as big as her head flitted past. The roars of thunder lizards echoed as if from nowhere. Yet that was not the most disturbing aspect of her visit. As she walked along the pathway, strange, chittering lizard-things clambered from their mosaic-lined pools to speak to her. One, a brightly coloured skink with a crown of long feathers, stretched a cold, scaly finger towards the centre of her forehead. She did not flinch, for her father had told her stories of celestial saurians as a child, and she had faced far worse things over her career as a witch hunter.

In a mind-wrenching psychic communion, the lizard-shaman showed her glimpses of what was to come. The city of Excelsis besieged. The walls tumbling. The sewers boiling. The rise of some hideous double-creature, squirming and foul like a larva ripped from a chrysalis, disgorged from a prison of crystal and mirrors. The city would be caught between the enemy within and the doom without. Yet of the latter, the skinks could see nothing but a cold, black void.

That strange absence, that gap in the cosmic tableau, kept the truth hidden entirely from their scrying. All they could perceive of it was a slow, ominous thump akin to the heartbeat of an elder god. But because the thing in the void was a mystery to them, because it had been so long removed from the tapestry of fate, it was impossible to read. Even in the last few days, when that void had pulsed ever stronger, some strange facet of its magic repelled their prophetic power. Consequently, the Seraphon of Mekitopsar would not muster to stand in its path – already their Scar-Veterans were waging a long war against the forces of Chaos abroad in Ghur, and they would not divert their warriors without solid guidance. Though it disturbed the skink priest greatly, it was the way of their people.

Such a swift and potent barrage of visions would have cost the mind of a lesser soul, but Doralia had an inner steel that no terror could crack. Back in the tavern, her tongue loosened by imported Aqshian liquor, she told her father everything she had learnt and more besides. Of all the dooms she had foreseen, the vision of a prison of mirrors had stuck with her the most – or, rather, the unforgettable image of the beings that slithered out of them. She had seen such a thing before, when making use of her glimmerings in the moments of peace before the city began to devour itself. That, said Doralia, was the threat the Order of Azyr had been created to forestall.

At dawn, the ven Densts, each profoundly glad of the wide-brimmed hats keeping the glaring sun from worsening their hangovers, made their way to the Consecralium. Built on a promontory at the edge of the city, the Stormkeep stood tall, its axe-blade profile stark and somehow accusatory as it jutted high into the skyline. Faint traces of lightning crackled around the beacon at its top. Upon their approach to its city-gate, Galen called out salutations and made the sign of the comet. For a long moment, the ven Densts were confronted by a wall of black rock, no reply but the cawing of gulls in the harbour. Then the lowest portcullis slid open. Behind it stood two tall, broad warriors in the white plate of the Knights Excelsior. They looked at the ven Densts for a long moment, then they escorted them inside.

Doralia shot Galen a wary look as the two silent guardians led them further and further into the vast Stormkeep's interior. Their passage wended not upwards, as they had expected, but down into the deep gaols below the city. Guttering torches crackled and spat with white fire. They passed cells within which mutant creatures writhed, captive greenskins battered iron grilles and sack-clad wretches gibbered in a dark tongue that rang in the ears. They made their way through a hall strung with chandelier wheels, each bearing a screaming, fanged body staked wrist and ankle so they hung dripping above boiling cauldrons of blood. Then, finally, they came upon the one they sought.

THE WHITE REAPER

The legends that surrounded Sentanus of Excelsis were dark and plentiful. An infamous Knight-Veritant, it was he who mercilessly purged those who would work against Sigmar – in many a dockside tavern, it was whispered that several innocents had too lost their lives, but Sentanus believed any sacrifice was worthwhile to stymie corruption. As they spoke, Galen ven Denst thought there was far more of the Nullstone Brotherhood about him than the Grand Conclave. With the Reaper's eyes boring into him, he began to wonder if he had made a colossal mistake – after all, one wrong word and he and his daughter would be rotting away in separate cells, never to see the light of day again.

It was only when Doralia made a full and impassioned disclosure of the prophecies she had gleaned from the Seraphon, along with the dilemmas that wracked the city, that the White Reaper's pitiless gaze turned aside. He said he had never so much as spoken to Maulgen, let alone given him his blessing, and that the zealot would pay dearly for his lies. As to the Seraphon, in his opinion, they were too alien to be any help at all. At this, the interrogator unclasped his mask.

The face beneath was craggy, seeming almost cast in stone. It was careworn, even more so than Galen's own weather-beaten face. For a moment, Doralia felt something almost like pity mingling with her fear. Here was a soul who had taken responsibility for the corruption that festered at the heart of the city and had been found wanting.

With shoulders slumped and gaze downcast, the White Reaper spoke at length about the greenskin hordes that had massed at the gates of the city. For years now, he had focused his energies on the Soulblight curse that had come to infect Excelsis; since the Time of Tribulations, each city had its own bane as a result of the Necroquake, and he had found out through lengthy investigation that a Neferatian coven had taken residence in the City of Secrets. In the years before that, Sentanus had dedicated himself to removing the Chaos threat, expunging Tzeentchian cultists wherever he had found them, and before that, he had rooted out the agents of the pirate lords of Bilgeport. Now came a clutch of new foes, each worse than the last. Even with the Astral Templars running their massed hunts out of Templia Beasthall to the east, the orruks were a constant menace. And here were two members of the Order of Azyr speaking of a new danger rising from within. Perhaps, he admitted, his focus upon the undead threat had blinded him to the greater danger – that of Sigmar's nemesis.

There came the dull crump of an explosion in the distance, and another, then a third. Dimly visible from the nearest arrow-slit in the Consecralium's wall, green fire blossomed near the docks. Stirring at the sound, the White Reaper finally replaced his mask, straightened his back with an almost palpable air of exhaustion and then strode out of the room. Galen and Doralia ven Denst shared another glance before following hard on his heels.

THEY CAME FROM BELOW

Excelsis echoed to a thousand screams as the sun set. The assault came not from within, where the strife in the streets had grown to violence, nor from without, where the walls were heavily defended in anticipation of a greenskin attack. Instead, when the eyes of the city's defenders were elsewhere, it came from beneath.

From culverts and sewer grates climbed an endless procession of slime-furred ratmen, each stinking and dripping with effluent. They shook themselves off like rain-sodden wolves before wiping their blades and darting off into the alleys. Across the dockyards, mushroom clouds of green smoke blossomed in the wake of ear-ringing explosions, and entire swathes of the street toppled into the sewers to expose the horribly glowing portals below. Hulking figures lumbered out from each baleful tear in reality, planting their clawed feet in the muck as they quickly established a defensive perimeter. Gnawholes, the clustered portals were called: splits in the fabric of the realms themselves from which the skaven launched their invasions. Rattachak, the Warlock Bombardier behind the attack, knew how to use them well.

The ven Densts pounded up the stairs from the Consecralium's dungeons and gained the lower ramparts for a better view. The prophetic glimpses of a writhing, brown river of filth became clear as slime-slick rats streamed out of each gnawhole by the thousand. Around the massive creatures defending the portals, each a grotesque fusion of flesh and metal with potent guns and wrecker-balls in place of hands, skaven warriors, half the size of the linebreaker monstrosities but a hundred times greater in number, chittered as they poured into the streets beyond.

The gun-toting skaven began opening fire on everything in their path. Rotary cannons whirred to spit glowing bullets that ripped the fronts from thronged taverns and decimated crowded markets. The smell of burning corpses filled the night as lightning crackled from strange contraptions, arcing out and grounding on the Freeguild companies rushing through the streets. Galen glimpsed a loose mob of bravos, off-duty soldiers, navvies and prizefighters, all drunk on liquid courage, barrelling out of the shattered taverns to charge the hulking rat-monsters. The most sober of them ripped away the hideous brain-rats couched in the apparatus upon the giants' backs even as their drunken comrades paid a bloody price for their bravado. Then a knot of maul-limbed creatures countercharged, and the brave militiamen were put down hard in a display of butchery so grotesque it turned even Galen's stomach.

Running hard to the gatehouse of the Consecralium, the ven Densts exited alongside several tight phalanxes of Knights Excelsior. In moments, the streets echoed to the stamping percussion of armoured feet as the Stormcasts split left and right to close the net on the gnawhole cluster. Though they had the advantage of knowing the city, their formations were bulky and, compared to the skaven, their numbers were few. Already there were ratmen

THE VOICE IN THE FIRE

Ever since he set light to his litter-nest as a hairless ratwhelp, the Warlock Bombardier Rattachak has always had a fascination with flames. To him, the smell of singed hair is like holy incense, the taste of charred corpses is the finest delicacy, torched buildings are his temples and his idea of sweet music is the screams of his burning victims. So dangerous is he that his fellows in the Clans Skryre keep him at arm's length, for he has been the doom of a dozen experiments since taking the role of Warlock Bombardier. One fateful night in Blight City, when he was chittering with glee into the fires of an old rival's burning warp-labs, he found the fire talking back. The greenish flames burned pink and purple as they conversed, and from the depths of his pyromaniacal obsession, a honey-sweet voice made him a bargain. It offered him the power to spread wildfire at will, the better to show others the glory of the burn. All it asked in return was that he raze the city of Excelsis at the appointed hour. Rattachak swore fealty to the strange voice then and there. From that day, he has had fires reflecting in his watery eyes even when none are burning anywhere near him, though those times are admittedly very rare. He has risen high in the ranks of the Clans Skryre, proving to be a superb demolitionist and amassing a coven of trigger-happy monstrosities that would follow him right into the heart of Sigmar's domain. Turning his obsession to ever more ingenious methods of ignition, he has devised a form of doomrocket that sprays liquid warpfire in all directions upon detonation. It is only a matter of time before he burns himself to a crisp, of course, but as long as his mysterious, silver-tongued patron sees him weaken the defences of Excelsis first, it cares not at all.

running along the rooftops, dropping through thatches and hide sheeting to attack the citizens cowering beneath. But they did not go unopposed.

Launching from high atop the Consecralium came Prosecutors borne on wings of light. Led by the Knight-Venator Malanea Lendu and her star-eagle Brightclaw, nine retinues descended in quick succession, hurtling like a meteor shower to spear their javelins and tridents through the darting skaven. The Prosecutors landed with crushing force, breaking distorted necks and skulls wherever they struck, then launched skywards once more to pull new weapons of crackling light from the stormclouds. The roof-runners they could not catch sent their triskele shuriken whipping into the streets below, each poisoned with foul concoctions of warpstone and gnaw-toxins. Those citizens not killed on impact were put down for good – not by the skaven but by eagle-eyed Judicators who had hustled to the crenellations of the Consecralium. The Knights Excelsior had no compunction in such acts, for even should the unfortunates survive, one so injured by warpstone could be corrupted by Chaos energy in mere hours.

It took most of the night to establish a cordon around the gnawholes near the docks, for the better portion of the Consecralium's strength was on crusade and the skaven were experts at attacking from the shadows. The priority was to corral the hulking machine-skaven that formed the shock troops of the invasion. Luckily, they appeared content to hold position whilst surrounded, instead causing as much property damage and arson as possible in defence of their beachhead. Behind them, teams of ratmen were hauling strange artillery pieces from the gnawholes; already they had constructed a kind of weaponry farm in the ruins of the Whaler's Rest. Any warrior of the Knights Excelsior who dared rush the position was disintegrated by a crackling beam of sickly green lightning, their essence flashing back to Azyr. When a group of Liberators split into six and charged the position from several directions at once, five were gunned down by ratling cannons, warpfire projectors and sparking lightning rays. For a moment, it seemed as if the sixth might break through the crossfire, leaping through the greenish flames with hammer raised high. Then the cackling skaven artillerist Rattachak let fly a corkscrewing doomrocket that hit him right in the gut, detonating in a deafening explosion of warp energy and leaving nothing but dissipating lightning behind.

The White Reaper ran hard towards the carnage, Galen and Doralia close behind him. Voice booming, the Lord-Veritant took command of the Stormcast position as soon as he reached it. A bulwark of Paladins formed up; he bade them clear the streets closest to the Consecralium until there was a clear route of reinforcement. Galen took to the roofs; Doralia climbed into the crow's nest of a large nautical tavern made from the remains of a landlocked galleon. There she took aim, racking and firing and racking again, each bolt hitting home between the eyes of a skittering skaven. Whenever her position was threatened, Galen defended the sniper's nest with utmost balance and surety: always moving, every pistol shot or sword thrust skewering a loathsome ratman as it made its attack. Below them, the White Reaper was death incarnate, fighting at the front of the cordon until his tally was as great as that of both the ven Densts put together. Yet no matter how many they killed, there were always more.

CHARGE OF THE KNIGHTS EXCELSIOR

Despite the Stormcasts' best efforts to contain it, the battle for the docks was spilling out into the city at large. The teeming multitudes of skaven in Rattachak's employ were in their element, slinking and stabbing and disappearing into the shadows whenever they sensed danger. But the real threat was yet to come...

To corner the scurrying skaven was to see the true viciousness of their kind, for when faced with no other option, the vermin-things fought like berserk wolves. It would be the work of months to dig them out, even if the main breach of their invasion were contained – and that was time that Excelsis simply did not have.

The White Reaper, fighting alongside Galen and Doralia, was doing everything in his power to stem the throbbing wounds in reality that were the skaven gnawholes. The Glimmerstretch – that main thoroughfare that ran through the city's heart – had been cleared by his Paladins; the citizens knew full well to stay out of the way of

Doralia watched Cerrus Sentanus impale one rat-thing even as he kicked back hard into the face of another sneaking round behind him, then she shot a third as it raised a dagger with its prehensile tail. She knocked its spasming body into the gutter with a snarl of distaste. 'Sigmar's bells,' she muttered. 'These things stink.'

On the roofs above, three of the creatures leapt across an alleyway with cat-like ease. One threw a volley of spinning metal triskeles at the White Reaper just as he took off his mask to wipe the clotted gore from its sockets. Wounded and on the brink of exhaustion, he did not see the projectiles in time, and they struck him in the side of the neck. Grimacing, he plucked them one by one from his flesh, pushing gauntleted fingers against the wounds to staunch them as he examined one of the bladed triskeles. Even in the flickering firelight, Doralia could see it was coated in a thin film of greenish poison. 'It's well known that you Stormcasts are tough,' she said. 'Are you immune to poison?'

'Not this kind,' came the reply. The White Reaper staggered, then, and sank to one knee.

'Up, Lord Sentanus,' said Doralia. 'The city needs you more than ever.'

The Stormcast did not reply but instead slumped with eyes unfocused, one hand in the gutter. Galen jumped down from his hunting-nest on the roof above, a trio of severed rat's tails in one hand. 'That doesn't look good,' he muttered. She cast him a glance, her lips pursed, and mouthed, 'It isn't.'

'My lord, we cannot yield,' she said. 'Who can possibly save this benighted place? Only the faithful, is that not your credo?'

Sentanus looked up at her, a spark of fire in his eyes once more. 'That's the Hallowed Knights, dolt. I am a Knight Excelsior.'

'Is it?' said Doralia innocently. 'Are they the ones who never give up?'

'The Hallowed Knights,' said Sentanus again, as if in a trance. 'The Steel Soul. He met one.'

Doralia winced. The warp-poison was clearly getting to his brain.

The White Reaper shot to his feet, staggering a little before looming within an inch of her face. 'He met one of them. The leader, the mage-priest. He could unlock this!' Sentanus clambered onto an upturned wagon and pushed himself up onto the roof of a mason's storehouse, using his lantern-stave as a support. Standing tall, he waved the staff high over his head to leave a glowing circle in the air. 'Malanea!' he shouted, his stentorian tones ringing out over the din of battle. 'Malanea, attend me!'

It took long minutes of agonising doubt, but to Doralia's relief, a winged angel swooped down over the mason's roof, a celestial eagle of impossible beauty glowing purple and blue at her shoulder.

'Malanea, we must get a message to Lord Gardus. He was bound for the Spiral Crux, and, with Dracothion's blessing, his aura should not be hard to find. Tell him the Starborne will not intervene here, but the mage-priest could be the key. It is the city's only chance of survival when the great siege begins!'

The Knight-Venator nodded, locking eyes with her cerulean familiar for a second before sending the creature skyward as a burning blur of light. Doralia found an expression of pure wonderment spreading across her features. Perhaps, she thought, as the White Reaper finally allowed himself to collapse, they would get their reinforcements after all.

their white-armoured protectors, and the hulking warrior elite made for an intimidating sight as they pitilessly slaughtered skaven invaders wherever they caught them. Only when the thunder of heavy cavalry shook the rafters of the docks did the scope of the White Reaper's plan become clear. Down the Glimmerstretch came an entire echelon of the Stormhost's Extremis chamber, voices raised in the clarion war cry of their kind – 'Era Draconis!' Wide-eyed citizens flattened themselves against the shells of burnt-out buildings as the Dracoth riders hurtled past.

Rattachak had not accounted for such a sudden assault; the idea of facing such a destructive heavy cavalry strike in a built-up area had never entered his mind, but to the Knights Excelsior, the collateral damage it caused was worth the cost. Perhaps if the shock troopers had been mounted upon simple destriers, the punishing firepower of the skaven gun-beasts would have mowed them down in disarray. As it was, the charge of the Thunderwave echelon saw some fifty tonnes of armoured Dracoth cavalry barrelling at top speed into the hail of warpstone bullets and billowing, green-tinged flame sent to meet them. Much of the fusillade was turned aside by the crackling energy that preceded the echelon like a bow wave, or else it was deflected by the massive, round shields of the Fulminators. When Rattachak launched another of his wildly twisting doomrockets, the detonation was eye-watering, yet on the Stormcasts came. No normal force could have withstood the killing beam of his warp lightning cannons, and indeed several of the leading riders were blasted limb from limb or gravely wounded to death. Yet their sudden discorporation into lightning left the way clear for their brothers and sisters behind – and the mounted Sacrosanct reinforcements behind them.

The remainder of the Thunderwave riders smashed in a blaze of lightning into the skaven position, lances and hammers bowling over even the largest of the skin-stitched monstrosities as their Dracoth mounts tore their pallid flesh to ribbons. The bloodshed that followed was horrendous, for though the monstrous skaven were exceptionally strong, armour-plated and bristling with weaponry, they relied on brute power alone. Against a well-drilled military force in their home territory, they had finally met their match. Within minutes, crack teams of Evocators mounted on Dracolines followed the assault. Chanting as one, they focused their abjurations upon the gnawholes themselves, forcing them to blacken and dwindle out of existence in a storm of warring energies, Rattachak squealed in dismay and anger. Squirting musk, he danced out of the way of his attackers and disappeared into the flames.

With the gnawhole cluster sealed and the White Reaper seeking reinforcements for the greater battle, Galen and Doralia briskly exchanged words. It was time for them to alert the Order of Azyr to Maulgen's duplicity and expose him and his inner cadre for the fraudulent fools they were – before the city burned in the metaphorical fires of civil war. There was just the small matter of the city's literal fires, plus its sudden infestation of ratmen, that stood between them and their goal.

FROM A DARK, UNHOLY UNION

Whilst the city's defenders fought fire and vermin, something vile and beautiful all at once peered from the other side of the mirror into the city's heart. An echo of far-off events had led to a new force of Chaos being born into reality, and it coveted Excelsis most of all.

In a dark and remote hollow of Ulgu, something impossible had taken form, a presence locked in a cursed wilderness where only contradictions could dwell for any length of time. The dual entity was known as the Newborn, and already it had adoring throngs of Hedonites worshipping it from afar. It was the offspring of Morathi in some ways and Slaanesh in others, whilst also being a strange blend of the two, for the prophesied Newborn had writhed into being as Morathi had achieved her long-held dream, slithering from the god-slit guts of its father at the peak of the High Oracle's duplicity.

At first, the entity had no set form; it was a half-real by-blow of the sovereign energies Morathi had bled from Slaanesh over the course of her apotheosis. As it hardened into a state that could exist in the material world, it found it could not settle on one form alone – an echo, perhaps, of its mother's split reality. The progeny was neither one thing nor two; it was both at once. It was a living soul-wound split into two shapes, two beings, by the symbiosis of dark and light, Ulgu and Hysh: the very same paradox that formed the chains of Slaanesh. In the dreams of the Dark Prince's worshippers, it would come to be known as Dexcessa, the Talon, whilst also being Synessa, the Voice. They were shadow and they were light, they were the subtlety of well-worded promise and the violent shock of direct action, but, most of all, they were excess.

For a time, Dexcessa and Synessa had been content to wait in the wings as the dust of Morathi's ascension settled. They had set themselves the task of orchestrating the downfall of Excelsis by proxy, in preparation for their grand entrance. They knew from their time as part of their father's consciousness that his rival Tzeentch had made a play for the City of Secrets – for he had coveted the prophetic potential of its glimmerings – and his plans had unravelled at the last. What sweeter insult, then, what finer gift to their progenitor trapped in Uhl-Gysh than to succeed where his brother in darkness had failed?

Being the children born from both the birth of a god and the undying hatred between Morathi and her godly nemesis, Synessa and Dexcessa were creatures of not only a dark beauty but also a deep and indelible self-loathing. At first, their forms were nothing more than a bubbling, pupal mass of energy set free from Slaanesh to streak like a fleshy comet across the sky during Morathi's great ritual. As they came to land in the hidden reaches of Ulgu, they began to split and coalesce, and just as the larva slowly grows into the butterfly, they each took a form of splendour and stunning dexterity.

Peering into the Mortal Realms, the Talon and the Voice watched the deeds of men and aelves with an all-devouring thirst. They found much to their liking, for there was an endless parade of conflict wrought in the name of this god or that, and all it took was a guiding hand, a whisper or a push to turn a righteous cause into the province of atrocity. Their icon was the broken mirror, for they considered themselves more beautiful than any other creature yet despised the very sight of their opposite number – who, in truth, was but the other half of the same soul. As they watched the Mortal Realms from beyond the shadow-mirrors of their oubliette, they projected this horrible, internalised hatred onto those who earned their ire, and in that bitter hatefulness, they found power. The power to enthral, to spellbind, to lend the gift of arcane skill in exchange for services to their wider agenda. They refined the ability to cast their will into the minds of others without them having an inkling that they were the puppet instead of the lord. So it was with Maulgen of Excelsis and, by extension, all who followed him. But he was far from alone in feeling their influence.

When the Knights Excelsior sallied forth to smash the skaven artillery position under Rattachak, the Warlock Bombardier resorted to that most common of his race's tactics under duress: he turned tail and ran. He had given in to the whispers in his mind, whispers that originated from Synessa the Voice, and hence brought anarchy to Excelsis, preparing the way for the greater doom to come by weakening its defences and setting as much of the city on fire as he could. In that, he already considered his mission a success. The entire dockyard area was ablaze despite the lashing rain, a swathe almost half a mile in width, and all it would take would be a change of the sea wind to see that fire run wild through the city. Not only that, but his allies in the Clans Eshin had scuttled and leapt into a thousand hiding places across Excelsis. Not even Rattachak knew that the triad of assassins at the head of the Gutter Runner invasion had a mission of their own, and behind it were the masters of manipulation who had enlisted his help in the first place.

Deep in the quarantined Crystalfall region, long-tailed figures darted across roofs and down alleyways, always keeping just out of sight. They closed in on the abandoned ballroom taken by Maulgen as his headquarters, clambering high onto burnt-out buildings to watch from behind broken chimney stacks and shattered Tzeentchian sky-craft. Screams and howled oaths came from within the rain-lashed ballroom as more aelven souls were slain in front of the mirrors that Maulgen and his fervent acolytes had confiscated, thinking they did so as a punishment for vanity and hubris. They knew not that in Ulgu, watching from the other side of the broken mirrors, Synessa and Dexcessa grew stronger on each unwitting sacrifice.

When the Brotherhood disbanded at the end of each execution, those same skaven snuck in and, in a blur of slingshots and perfectly pitched steel spheres, broke as many mirrors as they could until every reflective surface in the ballroom was cracked but still mostly intact. The triad of assassins at their head anointed each of the looking glasses with aelven blood – easy enough to find, given the number of slender corpses strewn around the place – and recited the words they had been given in their dreams. They would each be richly rewarded with the purest shadowstone, as fine a resource as an Ulguan spy could ask for, once the great and secret rite of summoning was complete.

That time came sooner than any anticipated. As wildfires raged in the distance, as the screams of aelves and men mingled in the streets and the prophecies of every soothsayer grew darker and more disturbing, hideous apparitions appeared within each of the broken mirrors and, as the blood of aelves slain by treachery slowly dribbled into the cracks, hauled themselves out like contortionists escaping from impossibly small confines. The greatest of the mirrors, confiscated from the former Grand Patriarch's dressing room and split jagged down the middle, shivered and sang as a thin red sheen of blood spread out all the way across it. From one half came Synessa, from the other Dexcessa. They spread their wings in the pelting rain, met one another's gaze, and smiled.

ACT II

THE RAMPAGE OF KRAGNOS

THE COAST OF TUSKS

The eastern coast of Thondia is prized by the Sigmarite creed, for the Spear of Mallus that juts from the Coast of Tusks is a heavenly gift more precious than the purest amberbone. Yet where civilisation rises, there too do the eyes of monsters fall…

Like ice lions circling a beached, wounded whale, the forces of damnation and disorder closed in upon Excelsis with hunger in their eyes. Here on the Coast of Tusks was a prize beyond measure: a well-established city with trade routes stretching north as far as the Talon Coast. The agents of Chaos who sought to bring it low worked from within; the civilians who sought most fiercely to protect it were doing the dark work of one of the Brothers in Darkness even as they put down the cults of another. Far less subtle but just as dangerous, the forces of Destruction gathered in ever greater hordes, the intent to smash the city to rubble. And they brought with them the means to do it. The high walls of Excelsis had withstood the fury of megafauna a hundred times over, but against that which was soon to come, they would be tested as never before.

THE CLAWING SEA
Haunted by oceanic monsters, even the aelves cannot truly tame this fearsome sea.

THE DESOLATE WILDS
From the hinterland mists come all manner of greenskin tribes, each hungering for war.

EXCELSIS AFLAME
Beset from within and without, this once-proud city suffered time and time again.
Clawing Sea
The Drench
Thunderscorn Peaks
Izalend
Icefangs
Thondia
The Great Gutfort
Great Excelsis Road
Coast of Tusks
Krondspine Range
Bilgeport
A swathe of mercenaries from the Meatfist Mawtribe departs the Great Gutfort to follow Kragnos.
Lake Everglut
The combined Waaagh! converges on Excelsis with deadly intent.
The Kraken-eaters of the coast gather to sack the city's docks.
Glossom Crevasse
More gargants leave their lairs to join Kragnos' growing entourage of behemoths.
Spear of Mallus
Excelsis
Krondskol
Breakface Mawpath
Morruk Hills
Skragrott enlists Breakface Mawtribe mercenaries and sends them ahead to reach the city and offer their services in its defence... for now.
Stone Nautilor
A swift-moving detachment of orruks is sent at double time to the coast, there to build a ramshackle fleet of wooden rafts and attack the city from the sea.
Questing Serpent River
Fraktoa Crevasse
Nautil Peaks
Lost Mesas
Ymnog's Trample (North)
Carcass Donse
Gordrakk's Waaagh! and the rampage of Kragnos clash in a titanic battle of dominance.
River Slannstongue
The Seraphon of Mekitopsar, already embroiled in a war against the forces of Chaos, do not intervene.
Koatl's Gullet
Mekitopsar
Primeval Jungle
Plains of Mekitopsar
Brokenjarl Mawpath
Greatpeaks of Andtor
Roving ogors of the Brokenjarl Mawtribe join the Waaagh! in the hope of a corpse-feast.
Lake Hoarfrost
Moulderpit
Ravening Rivers
Andtor
After exiting Bantu's Gate, Gordrakk's Waaagh! musters once more and heads north-east towards Excelsis.
Bantu's Gate

KRAGNOS, THE END OF EMPIRES

A monstrous deity of earthquakes and upheaval, Kragnos hails from a time long before Sigmar's reign in the Age of Myth. His fierce warrior spirit is said to embody the savagery of Ghur – small wonder, then, that the warlike nations of the greenskin race flock to follow him now that he is finally free from his arcane prison.

During the first primeval dawn of Ghur, the land was governed not by humans, aelves or duardin, nor even by greenskins, but by strange hybrid creatures that were as much animals as sentient men. Many of these were the spawn of the primordial essence of Chaos; known as beastmen, they claim to this day to be the true inheritors of the Mortal Realms. There were also those races whose existence was pure and free of any unnatural taint. Standing tall amongst them were the Drogrukh of the nation Donse: massive centauroid creatures that could trample even an ogor into the dirt without breaking stride. Native to the Ghurish Heartlands, the Drogrukh were creatures of earth and wilderness governed by a long and proud history. The one who rose highest of all amongst their culture was known as Kragnos.

Very little is known about Kragnos; the details of his existence are derived from crude paintings and charcoal depictions on the walls of Ghurish caves and from tales passed down from elder to skald in the oral tradition of the Ghurish Heartlands. The legends have it that Kragnos was once mortal, as with so many that have ascended to godhood over the aeons. He was born to the rulers of the Donsian nation, whose plateaus and mesas were hollowed out by the Drogrukh race until they formed caves large enough for even these boisterous, muscular creatures to live in relative harmony with the land. Over time, their culture grew strong; and they shaped the mesas with hand and hoof to form smooth-walled citadels crested with the eyries of their eagle messengers.

It was the way of the Drogrukh to only take what they needed, but the young Kragnos, born to the tribal elder Gorgos, wanted more. He had a simmering temper, and after being scolded for beating his brother to a pulp over the right to court the same mare, he decided to strike out with his closest companions. Together, the five Drogrukh stallions roamed the wilds of Thondia and the icy tundra of Bjarl, even scaled the Beastgrave in distant Lendu. They grew skilled in the arts of war, fashioning weapons from the streams of magma that exuded from mountains split by pounding hooves. The humans of that time lived in fear of Kragnos' rampages, but the orruks, impressed by his violent deeds, saw in him a great hero. As his exploits grew ever mightier, tales of 'Da Boss Trampla' were told by orruk shamans across the length and breadth of the Ghurish Heartlands. Each telling was more exaggerated than the last – and always with Kragnos, son of Gorgos, as the victor.

THE MAKING OF A DEITY

As the legends surrounding the giant warrior grew more impressive, he too grew in stature and power. Tales abounded of Kragnos strangling the Seven Serpents, of his hooves being shod with wreck and ruin, and of his victories over nation after nation that sought to end his rampages. Stories sprang up of how he tumbled the walls of Ur-Haracho through sheer anger, how he shattered Bjarl's southern coast to form its endless ice floes, and how he clawed up the ancient heart of rock from the largest geomantic nexus of Ghur so as to forge it into the head of his fell weapon, the Dread Mace. It was also said that Kragnos had retrieved the disc of the Shield Inviolate from a deep gouge in Ghur's crust – Gorkamorka had thrown it there in disgust, having tested its purity as a man would a coin of gold and chipped his tooth – and from the Twin-Headed God's blooded saliva, that great bronze shield had inherited the ability to eat magic. Called Tuskbreaker by Kragnos' orruk followers, it could repel the spells of Ghurish shamans as if they were no more than a breeze.

The orruks of that time had far more in common with the Bonesplitterz tribes than those of the Ironjawz; believing Kragnos to be a god, they offered up to him the bones of those monsters they slew as tribute. It was their fervent belief that the marrow of their sacrifices held the bestial spirit of Ghur itself. The Drogrukh lord was only too happy to crack those bones between his teeth and drain the juices – and, sure enough, some of the monstrous energy held within was imparted to him. Many an offering of amberbone was given up to him, too, the priceless realmstone crunched and swallowed

alongside the skeletons of slain monsters. As he sated his mighty appetite on the finest monster bone, he grew larger and more powerful. Indeed, his legend became a self-fulfilling prophecy: as even more impressive offerings were brought to him by the orruks that revered him, even more victories and successful beast hunts made their mark upon the wilderness of Ghur.

Kragnos grew accustomed to fighting alongside the orruks that followed in his wake, and he was pleased to find them chanting his name as he did so. He was happy to co-exist with the greenskins, for they respected strength, determination and stubbornness as much as he. Perhaps, on some subconscious level, he realised it was the orruks that were granting him a portion of his strength. Perhaps he merely tolerated them, as the caveman tolerates the wolf and feeds it scraps until it ultimately becomes his hound. Either way, over time, Kragnos became a feted champion of the orruks in western Ghur, thereby buying stability for his Drogrukh kin in the east.

The rise of Kragnos and his kin had seen him batter several barbarian nations to rubble, a feat that had earned him the epithet 'the End of Empires' amongst the people of Ghur. Word of his exploits had travelled via realmgate and portal across the lands, and millions if not billions of orruks from the realm's core to its edge spoke of his savagery. It was a favoured tactic of Kragnos and his companions to rear high and strike down with all the force of their combined mass at the same site, crumbling castle walls or even splitting the land itself as warriors fell back all around them.

After the Battle of Blood Gulch, a rumour gathered traction that Kragnos was a god of earthquakes, for a fissure had opened up and swallowed the monster-hunting barbarians of the Garagga even as they sought to bring him low. He was henceforth depicted in a myriad orruk lairs with the stony ground cracking beneath his hooves. Over time, as he grew ever mightier on a diet of amberbone and monstrous marrow, that same belief empowered Kragnos until reality began to echo the legend. Where his hooves slammed into the ground, the earth would yawn open. When wounded, he would bellow at the top of his lungs to send huts of wattle and daub – and later in his life, even bricks and mortar – tumbling down. The thunder of his stamping was echoed in the footfalls of thousands upon thousands of greenskins, and so, as time passed, the entirety of the Ghurish Heartlands was remade as his territory. The culling of humanoid prey became as nothing to him.

YESTERDAY'S ALLY, TOMORROW'S FOE

Kragnos' roamings eventually took him to the Draconith stronghold situated in the mountain range of Vexothia, said to be the fossilised spine of the Draconith's saurian predecessor. The Drogrukh champion remembered the drake-lords well, for he had fought alongside them as a youth against the Dragon Ogors of the Thunderscorn Peaks in the far north of Thondia. The Draconith were a race of scaled, dragon-like sorcerers born from the rocky peaks of Ghur, the eldest of which were each as large and powerful as the mightiest of the Drogrukh. Though there was no formal alliance between the two Thondian races back then, Kragnos' father Gorgos had brokered a non-aggression pact between the two nations. A war between the two elder races could only end in disaster, he reasoned. More than that, they had a common cause – their mutual hatred of the Shaggoth clans that claimed the mountains to the north.

Having come to Ghur from Azyr, the Shaggoths were a proud race. They could trace their origins to another realm, and yet they called themselves the rightful lords of Thondia. That in itself was enough to earn the ire of the native Drogrukh, who were fiercely protective of their supremacy over the Ghurish Heartlands. The Draconith, having learnt of the vile nature of Chaos from their patron Dracothion, hated the Shaggoths for having made a pact with the Dark Gods and turning their back on the natural order of things. Over the course of the War of Thirteen Peaks, the two races fought together for years and learnt the tongue of their allies in the process. Eventually, they drove the Shaggoths of the Thunderscorn Peaks to near extinction and, once they had broken their foe's power, went their separate ways in an accord of mutual respect.

This accord meant little to Kragnos, now at the height of his ambition. In the Draconith, he saw not respected allies of old but a new and challenging foe truly worthy of his stature. Together with his companions, he climbed high into the serried peaks and called out their challenge to the Draconith lords. He took the Dread Mace to their spire-tipped lairs, knocked down the statuary they had raised to the Great Drake, Dracothion, and kicked to death the giant mountain lions they kept as pets. It was a challenge that the Draconith could not ignore, and one that would ultimately see the end of not one but two elder empires. Yet that unreasoning, insane act of aggression won the approval of Gorkamorka.

Soon the mountain city of Vexothskol echoed to the din of war as Kragnos and his Drogrukh braves fought with everything they had to topple their rival empire. Several of Kragnos' companions used greatbows, spears and even massive throwing axes to cut down the drakes as they flew overhead. In return, Drogrukh flesh was roasted by amber fire or turned to stone by powerful arcane curses. One by one, both sides fell to their last few warriors. Through it all, Kragnos' rampage did not slow. The magic of the elder drakes rolled off Tuskbreaker like water, for the artefact made him impervious to even their most potent hexes and bolts. To attack him physically was to brave his crushing mace; dozens of the giant saurian beasts were sent, broken and cold, to an unmarked grave in the valleys below, but many gouged him deep with tooth and claw. When Kragnos' bellows of outrage toppled the citadels and statues, his pounding hooves splitting the mountaintops, it was the dragons that were forced to retreat. Taking their revenge upon Kragnos' remaining companions, killing them one after another with powerful magic, they winged off into the stormy night. Though Kragnos knew it not, they would give the last of their strength to crush the Drogrukh cities of Donse as their nation had been crushed in turn.

Kragnos was left alone amidst the ruin of the latest empire to fall to his hooves. He felt a great sorrow well up within him, for cast around him were the broken bodies of his closest friends, those who had fought as his captains in a hundred battles and more. Sorrow turned to rage, and he trampled every artefact, every entombed ancestor, every clutch of eggs he could find, hoping to eradicate the Vexothskol Draconith from history altogether. But he did not stop there: he hunted down dragonkind across all of the western heartlands – wherever he sighted the great winged forms, he would gallop at full speed across the plains after them until he had pursued them to their lair. There, the violence of Vexothskol was reprised, and another part of the Draconith empire was erased from history.

It was the last living drakes of Vexothskol that were to finally halt his vengeful onslaught. Their forefathers had known of another race that revered Dracothion, creatures of the heavens that rarely interacted with the rest of the Mortal Realms. The Draconith princes known as Krondys and Karazai, brothers united in blood as well as in their love of scholastic lore, had delved into the secrets of an ancient race of mage-priests and, in doing so, had uncovered a way to telepathically communicate with them – all such creatures called Dracothion their patron, and spiritually they were kindred.

Together, the two drakes entered a trance-like state in which they sought out an ancient intellect who claimed to hail from another world – from another time, in fact, as with so many of his kind. A vision of a regal slann appeared in their minds' eye. The being said he had once been known as Lord Kroak, though he had variously been called Quorac, Cro-Akk, Kribhet and a hundred other variations over his aeons-long existence. When told of the rampages of Kragnos, the slann's sceptre rose from his mummified hand to hover horizontally before him, then tipped upon its axis. The meaning was clear: balance must be kept, lest the rise of Destruction topple all else into the dust. On that day, a deal was struck. The drake-lords, their empire so near extinction after Kragnos had battered their strongholds to ruin, would hand their remaining eggs to the voidfaring temple-ships of Kroak and his fellow mage-priests. In return, the mage-priests would give all that they had to defeat the Earthquake God in whatever way they could.

VENGEANCE AT ANY COST

It was at Twinhorn Peak that the alliance of mage-priest and drake-lord confronted Kragnos. The Drogrukh god was so swollen on his diet of realmstone, monstrous marrow and constant conquest that the sides of the mountain sloughed away under his hooves as he climbed high to finish what he had started at Vexothskol. The battle did not go well for the drakes, nor the mage-priests, for still Kragnos' shield kept him inviolate, and he was near impossible to overpower in physical combat.

Kragnos roared in fierce exultation as he smashed the Dread Mace into one slann before crushing another against a cliff face with Tuskbreaker. The mountain shuddered as he gave vent to the seismic power of his wrath and it began to split under his hooves, the fissures under him turning into a crevasse and then a widening chasm that opened like a jagged maw ready to consume.

Only then did Kragnos realise that the peak on which he stood was not a normal rocky mass but the hollow granite horn of some colossal, long-dead creature. A swirling vortex of magic cascaded from the talons of mage-priest and drake alike; Kragnos looked up in a mixture of awe and horror as the crackling energies took the shape of the Great Drake Dracothion himself. The coiling, zodiacal godbeast constricted around Kragnos even as he leapt to intercept him, weathering the Drogrukh's frenzied attacks until it had his limbs locked tight.

Immobilised, his shield's anti-magic aura sparking violent green as it finally met its match in Dracothion's godly power, Kragnos was lowered downwards into a roiling sphere of energies that had gathered in the gullet of the mountain's opening maw. Around him hovered a dozen mage-priests like moons orbiting a realmsphere, each borne upon a palanquin of gold as they concentrated their immense arcane might on holding Kragnos fast for a few vital moments. The mountain, split open by Kragnos' own destructive aura as much as the warring arcane powers around the peak, closed once more. In doing so, it buried not only Kragnos but many of his assailants alive – a sacrifice deemed necessary by mage-priest, drake-lord and godbeast alike, for it entombed Kragnos in a hollow core of timelessness beneath hundreds of feet of granite. The spell of entrapment was woven of time itself and could not be damaged by mace, nor by might, nor by sheer outrage. Kragnos had been removed from the cosmic tapestry entirely by the magic of the Great Drake and his allies. But his incarceration would one day break, and on that day, his wrath would be mighty indeed…

THE RISE OF KRAGNOS

Aeons after his imprisonment, when the energies of Alarielle's Rite of Life spread their tendrils across Ghur, Twinhorn Peak shuddered and split down its axis. In that moment, the spell at its heart was broken, and a new force of upheaval was unleashed upon the Realm of Beasts.

Millennia had passed since Kragnos' incarceration within the great Ghurish peak. Though he had been rendered comatose by the spell that bound him, on some level, his destructive impulses could not be quenched. In his slumber, he had dreamed of wreaking havoc on all who sought to escape his mace, smashing cities and stamping fissures in the earth to tumble the works of those who would oppose him.

As the Drogrukh god languished, trapped within the rocky womb of Twinhorn Peak, empires rose and fell across the Mortal Realms. The children of prehistoric times rose gradually to master not only stone and bronze but iron, steel and realmstone. The centuries slid onwards; dynasties were formed and broken on the wheel of fate, but still Kragnos could not move a muscle. The last of the Draconith empire, dealt a mortal blow by the Earthquake God's butchery of their strongholds, dwindled into dissolution, with the draconic lords Krondys and Karazai fading into myth. Deep in the void, the core of Mallus hurtled from a bygone world, bearing a new god of humanity's warrior spirit to the Mortal Realms. On slept mighty Kragnos. The Age of Myth saw civilisation take hold in earnest, and the races of man, duardin and aelf raised cities so stunning that they would make a god weep with tears of joy. Then came the Age of Chaos, and all that beauty and progress was cast into the dust. Five hundred years later, Sigmar returned at the head of a new army, yet still Kragnos remained unaware, for in his sphere of timelessness, even the thunder of the God-King's tempest could not be heard.

Then, at last, came a shiver in the substrate of his tectonic prison. The arcane prison had held fast against the battering magic of the Necroquake, for what is the energy of endings against something removed from time altogether? Instead, it was the life magic of Alarielle that inadvertently set Kragnos free. The forest of stoneoaks that

had conquered the slopes high above his prison shivered as the Rite of Life broke across them, their trunks growing even taller and their roots digging even deeper into the mountain – so deep that their questing tips broke the rock that formed the mountain's heart. The magic that had bound the ancient being within dissipated, bleeding out from a hundred cracks to let the Drogrukh god uncoil, stretch and feel vitality flood his limbs once more – the same surging energy that had invigorated so much of the land itself as Alarielle's spell spread across the realm.

To destroy a mountain from the inside out, to batter through millions of tonnes of dense rock laid down at the formation of the realms, is a feat that only a god could have attempted. Even then, but a few could have hoped to succeed. Stubborn, lion-hearted Sigmar could have done it, perhaps, had he held Ghal Maraz in his fist. Gorkamorka, his strength that of all the greenskins in all the worlds combined, would have relished the challenge. Kragnos, meanwhile, took his might from relentless, elemental savagery. Over and again, his mace battered the interior of the sphere that had held him – *thump, thump, thump*. The noise echoed through the strata of the land and the dreams of shamans, visionaries and warmongers. Smashing his way through the mountain, he reached the mummified slann corpses that had kept the spell of timelessness intact and crushed them to scattered bone and powdered flesh. *Thump, thump, thump* went the Dread Mace, making easy work of even the densest rock. *Thump, thump, thump* went the stamping feet of Bonesplitter tribes across all of Ghur, echoing its crushing impacts. Soon, war drums were beaten in time with the steady rhythm, though the greenskin drummers knew not what compelled them to do so. And all the while, in his long war against the mountain that had swallowed him, Kragnos did not rest.

Under the light of the Bad Moon, the End of Empires battered his way free of his prison with a deafening bellow of triumph. The rubble of Twinhorn Peak tumbled around him as he broke through the peak's flank, the mountain finally defeated. He hauled himself through the rockslide of his own creation, bloodied and covered head to toe with rock dust. Then, with a great roar of exertion that sent avalanches cascading down the slopes of the Ursricht's Kill mountain range, he climbed the remnants of Twinhorn Peak and, with one final heave, stood atop the wreckage and ruin of his prison to bellow his defiance at the sky.

Soon, all of Ghur would shake to the intensity of his wrath.

SKRAGROTT'S MUSTER

All across the Ghurish Heartlands, the hills and rugged mountains resounded to the drums of war. Pointed green ears everywhere pricked up at the rhythm, whether heard as echoes from a distant horizon or experienced only subconsciously.

Slumbering greenskins found their heartbeats falling in time with the pounding rhythm as they dreamed of conquest and unending, joyous battle. What the distant life-song of Alarielle had begun, and what the hooves of the Earthquake God had reinforced, the very spirit of Ghur had echoed and imparted to uncounted hordes of its green-skinned children.

That raw energy and surging life force became something warlike and fierce among the orruks. The Bonesplitterz in particular found it reverberating around their skulls with ceaseless, mind-altering clarity, for they were the most attuned of their kind to the raw energies of the gathering Waaagh!. Wardokks and wild-eyed shamans saw cloud-shapes in the form of half-stallions, leering shields and toppling towers; to them, the message of war was especially clear. Eight days after Kragnos had broken free, the famed Aqshian Warboss Gulgaz Stoneklaw came through the portal of Bantu's Gate at the head of a thousands-strong horde of Bonesplitterz, the shrunken heads of his advisors, worn on his shoulders, glowing green with primal magic. He gave a roaring speech to those around him – short and basic but with vigour enough to inflame the soul. The time of war was close.

Stoneklaw was not the only outrealmer to have been drawn to the source of the relentless beat. Emerging from the frozen wastes of the Shatterland Floes came a troggherd from the Spiral Crux in Chamon, led by the towering, seaweed-draped creature known as Glogg. That barnacle-dotted beast had no real intellect to speak of; rather, he followed some idiot-savant instinct as to where the best fighting was going to be – even if that meant setting off years in advance. Though his odyssey was entirely unconscious, it had led him to Ghur in time to join the growing Waaagh!. With him came a trailing, mile-long mob of troggoths of all kinds, a madly bouncing horde of squigs hopping along in their wake.

From half a hundred lairs across the Ghurish Heartlands, gargants lumbered into the sunlight, scratching their bellies and picking their noses in deep thought as they squinted at the horizon. Something was coming; even their dim-witted minds could tell that. Perhaps it was time for the true Son of Behemat to take up his crown and become a godbeast. Those who saw Kragnos as an impostor or a rival met him in battle – and were mercilessly crushed.

In Rondhol, across the Mawbight from Thondia, the distant drumbeat was heard in the minds of two great greenskin warlords who had joined forces to sack the stronghold of the Tuskvault. The first was none other than Gordrakk, the Fist of Gork: he who had united the Ironjawz clans and who rode to war on the mightiest living Maw-krusha, Bigteef. The other was a squeaky-voiced runt who, without his hat, struggled to stand five feet tall even on tiptoes. Yet it was the latter, the infamous Moonclan warlord Skragrott, who was to shape the destiny of the Waaagh! to come.

SKRAGROTT, LORD OF THE MOONCLANS

The king of the Moonclan grots rules not through might but through cunning. Claiming to all who will listen that the Bad Moon spoke to him once (just once), Skragrott has positioned himself as the foremost prophet of the belligerent lunar god-thing worshipped by all his troglodytic kind. Conniving and cut-throat, he has risen so high in grot society that he now claims the rust-mountain of Skrappa Spill as his sovereign domain and not only commands numberless hordes of black-robed grots – his 'Konkererz' – but also counts whole tribes of orruks and ogors amongst his allies. The secret of his uncanny foresight is his fungal asylum, a weird otherworldly sub-realm where he keeps those true seers he captures in a mushroom-addled state of delirium from which he can harvest their visions. During the Siege of the Tuskvault, Skragrott showed a measure of his magical power as the chosen of the Bad Moon, in doing so solidifying an alliance with Gordrakk himself. It was an uneasy partnership, but one that was to lead to a new era.

The Drogrukh god made his way down the ruin of the ancient mountain, rubble powdered to dust with his every footfall. A hundred scratches and gouges covered his hide, godsblood stark crimson against the ochre dust of the mountain's demise. Still his bearing was proud; still he bore the Dread Mace in his fist. He unlimbered the shield Tuskbreaker from his back and strapped it to his arm, using his teeth to pull its band tight, then rolled his shoulders with a series of muscular cracks.

'No weakling, I,' growled Kragnos. 'I fought the Serpent and won.' The words, hoarse as they were, sounded good. 'I broke its prison.' He spoke to himself as much as to the mountain, testing his voice after being so long dormant. It was a dry, choking rumble, like distant thunder, but it grew in power with each syllable. 'I claim my birthright.'

He could feel some of his legendary strength returning, flooding through his limbs as his blood pumped hard, pulsing through veins as thick as oaken boughs to set his great fists clenching. The urge to wreck something, temporarily sated by the death of the mountain that had imprisoned him, was rising fast. He took a deep breath, filling his lungs with the dusty Thondian air. It tasted different, somehow. The Ghurish wilds had a musty tang of cairns and dead things, but it was dissipating, as if blown away on the wind before a spring storm.

'My kingdom,' he said to himself. He climbed up the scree of the nearest peak, his hooves crunching deep with each footfall, his gait growing steady as a mountain goat. Within minutes, he had climbed to the summit, landslides pouring in his wake. He would grind the whole mountain range to gravel if he had to, in order to lay his rightful claim upon the land.

There, where the mountain's flanks should have lain in tumbled disarray, an ancient forest covered the lower slope. He could dimly discern the shape of the mountain beneath; it was only a few weeks since he had toppled it, after all. Or so he had thought. He frowned, his worst suspicions slowly dawning.

Making his way around the side of the peak, he looked far to the east, expecting to see the tall mesas and plateaus of his native land, Donse, jutting over the horizon. He had fought hard to secure their pre-eminence, laying low a dozen rival empires for his own to thrive. Perhaps they had become the rulers of this land and had shaped it to their wishes, as was their right.

The towers of Donse were not there. Instead, the Thondian coast to the north-west had risen high, pushing its way to prominence over that part of the horizon that should have been dominated by his homelands. Upon that coast, glinting in the sunlight, were the spires and towers of a distant city. A city of men.

Kragnos' nostrils flared, his eyes wide at the sight. He felt his heartbeat quicken as a killing rage came upon him. Its thump was loud in his ears, an urging, insistent tattoo that demanded satisfaction through acts of wreckage and destruction. Far off, on the plains below, he heard the rhythmic boom of war drums echoing in time.

A roar grew deep in his chest, alive with bellicose vigour and desperate to get out. He gave full voice to it, the mountains shivering in fear as his anger reached a terrible crescendo, echoing across the Ghurish Heartlands from end to end.

The time of ruination had come.

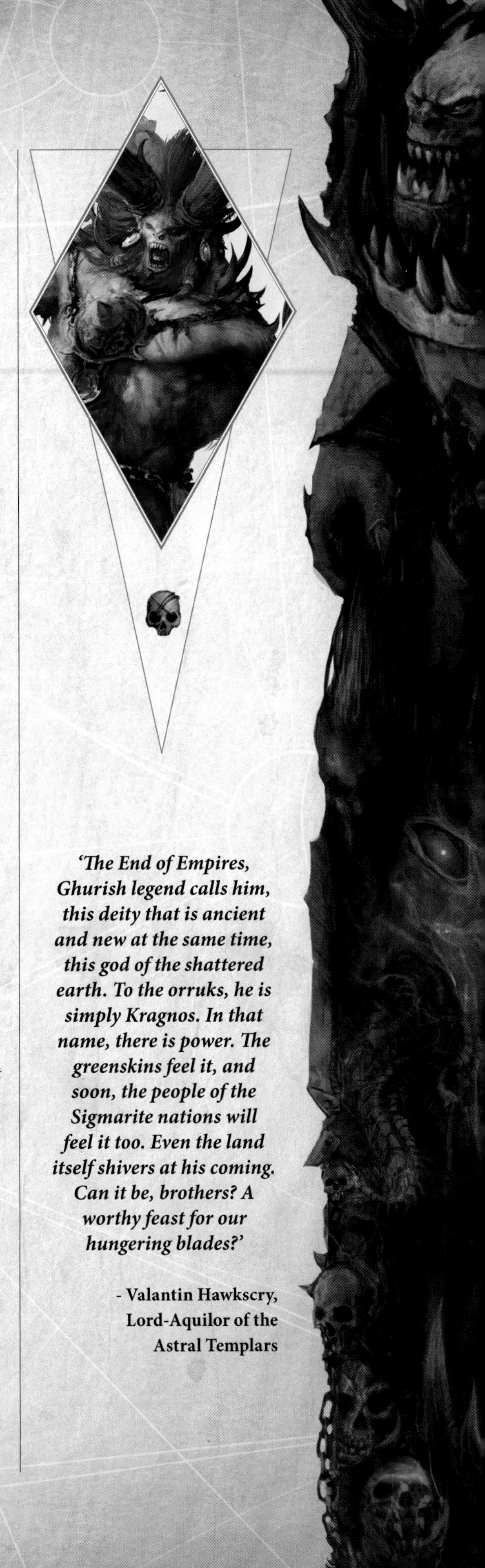

'The End of Empires, Ghurish legend calls him, this deity that is ancient and new at the same time, this god of the shattered earth. To the orruks, he is simply Kragnos. In that name, there is power. The greenskins feel it, and soon, the people of the Sigmarite nations will feel it too. Even the land itself shivers at his coming. Can it be, brothers? A worthy feast for our hungering blades?'

- Valantin Hawkscry, Lord-Aquilor of the Astral Templars

ON THE WARPATH

The greenskin tribes of Ghur have always been the most savage and dangerous of all its peoples, but such is their love of war that without a strong leader, they would turn to fighting amongst themselves and expend their strength. When united as one behind a single warlord, however, nothing can stop their rampage.

It was Skragrott the Loonking who gave the mustering greenskin hordes a new sense of urgency and focus. It had been he who had summoned the teeth of the Bad Moon to crack open the Tuskvault of Rondhol, though the actions of the Fyreslayers who defended it caused the entire structure to collapse before the legendary Basha Shard could be retrieved. The forces of Gordrakk could have considered this a great setback, for the shard was said to have come from Gorkamorka's own club and they were all looking forward to seeing what it could do in the hands of the Fist of Gork. However, the orruks had enjoyed a fantastically intense battle outside the Tuskvault, opposed as they were by an alliance of the Hammers of Sigmar and the Fyreslayers, and they were still riding high on the sheer spectacle of the disaster they had unleashed. To them, the fight was the main thing, rather than the prize at the end of it.

Skragrott did not see it that way. He had invested a great deal of effort in learning the prophecies and omens that surrounded the rising, thumping drums of war he could hear in his troubled dreams. For once, he had the clarity of prophetic insight he had always claimed to possess, and he intended to capitalise upon it. Over the last few months, he had mercilessly bullied more detail out of the captive scryers and prophets in his fungal asylum. By securing a quantity of glimmerings from an Excelsian trading caravan and force-feeding them to the most lucid of his imprisoned seers, he had precipitated a set of visions that very much suited his intent to become the power behind the greatest greenskin throne of all. A mighty orruk warlord was to rise, wielding three sacred artefacts of power, and he would use them to smash apart the greatest city of men in all of Ghur. In doing so, he would unite the tribes and capsize the Realm of Beasts in a new era of war. Skragrott fully intended to help this come to pass – and then make himself the brains of the greenskin empire that would claim the Realm of Beasts once and for all.

First of these prophesied artefacts was the skull of a godbeast, plucked from the lair of the Spider God's children. That part of the prophecy had already

been fulfilled. In the chasm-like Crawling Pits of Gharrentia, Gordrakk had ventured deep into the earth, fighting his way through not only a colony of massive, chitin-armoured Arachnarok Spiders but also a brotherhood of Astral Templars sent to defend the tumbled Stormvault of Thunderstone Reach. Amidst those darkened, humid ruins, Gordrakk wrested a bloody victory, and as his trophy, he hauled free no less a relic than Hammergord, the skull of an ancient godbeast with a bull's head and a heart of fire. This he had fashioned into the largest iron battering ram that Skragrott had ever seen; it was said that Hammergord's horns had the power to shatter mountains, and Gordrakk had plans of his own for its use.

The second relic of which his prophets had spoken was the Basha Shard. This, unfortunately, remained out of his reach, for the Tuskvault that had held it had collapsed. Rather than risking his own scrawny neck in urging Gordrakk to stick around long enough to dig it out, the Loonking sent his foremost prophet – the infamous Snazzgar Stinkmullet – to deal with the Fist of Gork in his stead. A powerful Cave-Shaman noted for leading a foray against Nagashizzar during the Time of Tribulations and then escaping back to Ghur in the resultant carnage before the Shyish Nadir could claim him, Stinkmullet was as old, wrinkly and tough as an elder deffcap mushroom. So renowned was his wisdom that even Gordrakk agreed to give him an audience – or perhaps he simply did not care enough to kick him out. The cunning of Mork, as embodied by Skragrott and his prophets, was soon to be united with the sheer brute force of Gork, wrought in the form of orruk muscle and battered metal by Gordrakk and his Ironjawz. Truly, it is said that on that day, Gorkamorka himself smiled.

'Ya gotta get that Basha Shard, boss. It's all part of da prophecy, ya see.' Snazzgar kept his eyes down, as Skragrott had taught him. Wasn't a good idea to make eye contact with the Fist of Gork, the Loonking had said. The shaman kicked back his pet spore-squig, Parpa, hoping it wouldn't stink up the cavern too bad, and set his features in an ingratiating grin.

Gordrakk turned towards him with a creak of grinding metal but said nothing. Snazzgar could feel the weight of his gaze like an iron gauntlet squeezing his skull. The shaman's bladder felt horribly full all of a sudden, but he held his ground.

'You grots and your "proper-see",' growled Gordrakk eventually, looking back out of the mooncave at the shattered vault beyond, where his prize lay buried. Snazzgar let that hang in the air, wise enough not to say a word.

'Gotta say,' mused Gordrakk, 'I woz lookin' forward to tryin' out da club-shard. Woulda been fun.' He thumped his Maw-krusha on the side of its head. 'We like a bit o' fun, don't we, Bigteef? Like killin' big-mouthed grots. That's always good fer a bit.'

The Maw-krusha growled, a sound like rocks tumbling in a chasm. Despite the fact he'd personally led an army to Ol' Boney's door, Snazzgar was still deathly afraid of the beast. One day, thought the Cave-Shaman, he'd be the one wearing the bosscap crown. Brokering a deal with the Fist of Gork was all part of it.

'Yeah, that's da fing,' said Snazzgar. 'Once we dig up the shard, we gotta get the uvver bit wot we need. Da Golden Amulet, the shrooms called it.'

'Wossa amulet?' said Gordrakk, still staring out at the tumbled mountainside of the Tuskvault.

'It's like a trophy, innit,' said Snazzgar. 'Proper shiny like. Wear it round yer neck, and nuffink can touch ya.' He held up a wizened crow's foot, a talisman from a bird that had fallen dead out of the Shyishan skies – it had been a good omen at the time, given that he had been rather hungry. 'It's like a boss trinket. Only for da best Megaboss who ever bossed.'

'Right,' said Gordrakk. Snazzgar felt like there was a rook's egg stuck in his throat as the Megaboss slowly reached down to the cave floor and picked up an enormous jagged choppa. 'Fing is, ya can't kill someone wiv a fancy necklace.'

'Er,' he said. 'I can guide you to it nice and quick, boss, once you lot've dug out the Basha Shard, then after the amulet, it's on to Excelsis like you planned. Won't take more than—'

'Shut it,' said Gordrakk, spinning round with red fury in his eyes. Snazzgar squealed in animal fear as the orruk lunged across the cave, his axe held high. The Cave-Shaman staggered back, but not far enough; the giant mushroom he wore as a hat got in the way. The choppa shattered his ribcage and spattered his vital organs all over the wall.

'Sod the Basha Shard,' said Gordrakk. 'Sod yer magic shrooms, and sod yer stupid amulet.' He hoisted up the dying grot's body as if it weighed no more than rags, lobbing it over to his Maw-krusha. Snazzgar was dimly aware of sailing across the cave before the beast caught him in mid-air and ended his life with a satisfied snap.

'We're going straight for the humie city, Bigteef,' said Gordrakk, 'And then we're gonna trash it into the dirt.'

THE JOURNEY EAST

Gordrakk's path across Ghur was guided by two things: his relentless desire to destroy every challenge to his authority and his impatience to do so as soon as possible. Travelling as the crow flies would have meant spending time crossing the Bitingsea and the Mawbight. Luckily, Skragrott knew of a shortcut.

To the north-east of the Tuskvault was a realmgate known as the Gaping Portal. In form, it looked like the jaws of some titanic shark, and from between its myriad fangs poured the Sharptooth River. Those strong or cunning enough to wade upstream without getting ripped to shreds and dive into the darkness between the jaws emerged from Bantu's Gate in southern Gallet, the nation to the south of Thondia, where Excelsis glimmered on the eastern coast. It was a testament to the galvanising will of Gordrakk that hundreds of thousands of orruks and grots followed him from the disaster of the Tuskvault and plunged through the Gaping Portal, heedless of the rumours that it would eat them alive. A few thousand were torn apart by the Sharptooth River, but the rest were spat out again, hale and whole but mightily confused, on the other side of the Ghurish Heartlands.

Once more the muster gathered, and once more the greenskin tribes under the Fist of Gork darkened the plains. The gargants given the duty of carrying Hammergord, that vast battering ram made from the skull of a bull-like godbeast, picked up their burden once again, and the drums of war thundered until every greenskin for miles around had the urge to find something to kill. Gordrakk had a target in mind, one that would likely lead to the biggest scrap with the hated 'humies' that he could find. He insisted they take the straightest route to Excelsis, despite his grot scouts telling him that it would take them perilously close to Mekitopsar – a thick and deadly jungle prowled by lizards that walked as men – and into the haunted valleys of Carcass Donse. But insisting upon things was something Gordrakk was very good at, and Skragrott was wise enough not to gainsay him – not directly, at least.

The Loonking's captive seers had given him troubling details of a vision that each of them had shared – a green fist being crunched knuckle and finger between the jaws of a giant, saurian monster – and the idea of facing the star-monsters of the Seraphon did not appeal to him one bit. He enlisted the aid of some old allies: the Shyishan Spiderfang known as the Grimscuttle, currently employed as the horde's outriders. They changed the crusade's heading, slowly and almost indiscernibly, so it gave a wide berth to the Mekitopsar jungle and instead forged into the Mawpath of the Brokenjarl ogors. It was a sneaky trick to avoid conflict in this way, and if Gordrakk ever found out he had been misled, it would be a fatal one. But it was a ploy that likely saved tens of thousands of greenskin lives and added a powerful tribe of ogors, Gutbuster and Beastclaw alike, to their number. Within weeks, the more intelligent of their number had been gathered together and sent on a mission by Skragrott, who promised them the finest of spoils if they pulled it off.

The growing Waaagh! pushed forward with deadly momentum. Just less than a month after Gordrakk emerged from the portal in the south of Gallet, he stood on the lip of the vast canyon that was all that was left between him and the Coast of Tusks. Cross the chasms and mesas of Carcass Donse, and Excelsis would be within reach.

Perhaps it was simple misfortune that saw the Waaagh! reach that ancient land at the same time as Kragnos. Perhaps it was the influence of Gorkamorka. Either way, as Gordrakk arrived at the edge of what had once been the centre of the Drogrukh empire, he saw a giant centauroid warrior roaring and stamping in anger – and swiftly resolved to kill it.

CLASH OF GIANTS

Kragnos, after breaking free from his prison of timelessness, had resolved to do two things: one, fight his way across the land to Donse and re-unite with whatever was left of his people, and two, break down the city of men that seemed to be claiming the Coast of Tusks for its own. He had made his way across the Ghurish Heartlands at a headlong gallop, leaving the ground splintered and torn in his wake – partly because he did not want to spend a single moment more than necessary away from his people, and partly for the sheer joy of running after so long in his anachronistic gaol. From above, he appeared to be galloping at the tip of a great jagged fissure that, racing across the wilderness, split the land of Thondia in two. He likely would not have stopped on his rampage were it not for a clan of Mega-Gargants known as the Gallet Stomp.

The Gallet Stomp hailed from the land of Big Dent to the east of Vexothskol. The bad-tempered heel who led it from one crushing massacre to the next was

called Huge Thargo, and though he was becoming hard of hearing in his autumn years, he ruled his clan with an iron fist. Accompanied by his sea-loving uncle Derko Walrusbiter and his three brothers Heb, Nonko, and Sorg the Broke, Thargo had been the scourge of the Gallet wilderness for decades. He was still picking the remains of an Excelsian caravan's defenders from between his toes after a particularly vicious squishing when he heard the thunder of hooves to the north. It was the first sound he had heard clearly for years.

When Thargo first saw Kragnos galloping towards him, he thought he had found a gargant on a huge mount. Only when he charged in, raising the iron-banded oak tree he used as a club high, did he learn his error – this was not two creatures but one. In that moment of hesitation, his fate was sealed. His club rebounded off Tuskbreaker, shattering into splinters even as the Earthquake God shouldered him aside. With a vicious backhand blow, Kragnos broke Thargo's spine with the Dread Mace, roaring in triumph as he galloped past. Heb was next to pay the price of ambition, his head staved in by Kragnos' thrashing hooves as the deity reared into the air. Sorg the Broke moved to flank him, only to find the ground splitting under his feet as Kragnos' hooves hammered back down. His ankle snapped as the earth gave way, making Sorg easy prey for the Dread Mace. Nonko got a good hit in with his crude flail, raking the Drogrukh god's side, but Kragnos' blood was up and he felt nothing but outrage. With a deafening bellow, he turned Nonko's brain to mush before goring the gargant on his curling horns. Derko Walrusbiter was the only one wise enough to kneel before Kragnos, offering up his shipwrecker club as a knight proffers his sword to his liege. Kragnos grunted low and guttural – *good enough* in the ancient Drogrukh tongue – and let the old Mega-Gargant live.

Derko was the first of the giants to join Kragnos' side, and he was far from the last. By the time the Earthquake God reached the edge of the vast canyon-like landscape of Carcass Donse, he had a dozen of the monstrous oafs in tow. Yet they were not truly his people. Soon, he told himself, he would be back amongst the Drogrukh.

The End of Empires had finally returned to his homeland, only to find it ground to dust. It had been toppled first by the drake-lords and then by the slow but insatiable ravages of time. There was nothing left of his once-proud nation save a vast chasm, consumed by the continent of Andtor on one side and Thondia on the other. And of his people, there was no sign at all. The only living things Kragnos could see were greenskins amassing a few miles to the south, their leader a hulking brute atop a scaly behemoth. If they thought to claim the sorry remnants of Donse for their own, they would not live to see another day.

Amidst the time-shattered ruins of Carcass Donse, Kragnos vents his fury on the one warrior hard-headed and tough enough to fight him to a standstill – Gordrakk, the Fist of Gork.

'Us orruks follow da biggest and hardest of da lot. There's none of this humie nonsense wiv shiny trinkets and big hats, never knowin' who's da boss of wot. Yer might follow someone dead cunnin' instead, for a bit, but when it comes right down to it, it's the one that can bash ya to bits wot calls the shots.'

- Grokko, orruk tactician

'There he is, Bigteef! Get 'im!'

Skragrott watched in awe as Gordrakk and his giant, scaled monstrosity bowled through the ochre dust of the chasm towards the roaring, horse-bodied monster. The Loonking gulped. He had seen that thing depicted on cave walls and had a nasty feeling it was an actual god.

He had a great vantage point, up here on the lip of the chasm. Purely for tactical overview, he told himself. Not because the great canyon's bottom had turned into a terrifying meat grinder of sharp metal, orruk muscle and gargantuan monstrosities intent on killing each other. The din of the fight, echoing from the great canyon walls, was deafening. He could see the Bad Moon rising to the west, slinking out like a hungry wolf from behind the dark pall of Ulgu to watch the fight. Its blessings fizzed in his blood and made his fingernails itch.

A trio of lesser gargants closed in on Gordrakk, kicking aside the Bonesplitter orruks that intercepted them. One of the gargants tried to pull Gordrakk from the back of his steed; the Fist of Gork took his forearm with one axe and his head with the other, a fountain of gore spattering high into the air. The second kicked Bigteef squarely in the face – a blow that could have shattered a castle wall. The Maw-krusha growled and lunged forwards, jaws clamping around the gargant's waist to bite down hard. It shook its prey like a crocodon does an antelope, flinging aside the brute's upper half as it messily devoured his legs with a series of horrible crunches. Gordrakk laughed loud and raucously as the third gargant turned and ran, then he waved his Gore-grunta cavalry to go after him. Shame, thought Skragrott. Gargants were great in a siege, and the hordes would be at Excelsis in a matter of weeks. If any of them got out of Donse alive.

The galloping god was pounding through the press, its hooves flattening armoured orruks left and right. Crackling green energy cascaded across its shield as Gordrakk's shamans hurled spells and hexes at the creature to no effect. A knot of troggoths, too stupid to read the odds, piled in towards it. One landed a solid blow before they were all burst like sacks of vomit by the creature's knobbled mace. In the beast's wake, the earth itself broke apart, plumes of dust and pools of gore showing the messy red path of its progress.

As the god-thing rounded a pillar of rock, Gordrakk kicked Bigteef into a charge. Both combatants gave their war cry. Gordrakk's was taken up by a hundred thousand greenskin throats; the titan's was loud enough to drown them out, tumbling the edges of the chasm to crush hundreds of orruks below. Skragrott felt a manic grin peel back his lips, half in nervousness, half in sheer glee at seeing two giants of war fight face to face.

The monstrosity attacked first, its great mace swinging towards Bigteef's head. The scaly behemoth deflected the blow on instinct and got a broken wing for its trouble. Gordrakk roared in savage battlelust; as his foe had struck, he had leapt to grab its arm like some armoured gorilla, swinging upwards and away from Bigteef. Gordrakk hacked at the titan's wrist with his green-glowing choppa, laughing madly. Bigteef lunged, jaws open, to sink its spade-like fangs deep into the god-thing's chest. The beast roared in pain as it brought the rim of its shield down hard onto Bigteef's skull, but the Maw-krusha's jaws were locked tight. Again the shield cracked down; still Bigteef did not yield.

The titan, unable to dislodge either Gordrakk or his steed, brought the orruk in close, its jaws open wide. The Fist of Gork shoved his other axe in the creature's mouth, breaking teeth and slashing its tongue in a spurt of bright red. As the beast spat out the axe, he climbed onto its shoulder and headbutted his foe right between the eyes with a dull thump of bone. The great centaur reeled in surprise. Sensing an opening, Bigteef released its jaws, lunging again for a killing bite.

It was a critical mistake. The beast-god swung its shield arm out, backhanding Bigteef away and slamming its mace into the Maw-krusha's chest with a one-two strike. The scaly monster was crushed against a huge spire of rock, the anvil to the titan's hammer blow, and the entire edifice came down as a tumble of boulders, crashing onto the three combatants with a deep rumble. Bigteef was buried in an instant, and even the centaur went down hard; Gordrakk rolled away, bloodied and bruised, in a clatter of iron. The titan was the first to recover, getting half up with a tooth-loosening roar of indignation to stamp towards the fallen Fist of Gork. Skragrott watched, the fierce energy of battle coursing around his mind as Bigteef shook himself free of the rock and muscled forward, broken but angry. The centaur kicked out with its hind hooves, clipping the side of the great beast's temple. The Maw-krusha shuddered and was still.

Gordrakk stood, defiant, his last remaining axe held loosely in one hand as the shadow of the vengeful god fell across him. Skragrott had enjoyed the fight, but he had invested too much in his fragile alliance with Gordrakk for him to be squished into a paste. A scream forced its way from the grot's throat, and he flung his arms skyward just as the Bad Moon flickered and pulsed high above. Tooth-shaped fangs of rock hurtled down from the dimming skies, thudding into the Donsian earth like a palisade barrier in front of the beast-god. It paused, staring down balefully at the orruk before it, then turned to look straight at the leering moon. A long moment stretched out. Skragrott felt like he aged a year as the world held its breath.

Then the titan grunted, debris cascading down its shoulders, and started to walk north towards the Coast of Tusks. After a while, the god-thing turned back and looked at Gordrakk. Holding the orruk's gaze, it pointed that massive, awful mace in the direction of Excelsis and turned away, beginning the long climb out of Carcass Donse.

'You heard him, lads,' roared Gordrakk, a killing light still blazing in his eyes. 'We got a city to smash!'

'The glimmerings showed so many fates, that year. So many waking dreams they had for us. But even in the most meagre vision, it could be discerned – if you were looking for it. The ground underfoot was always trembling, as if in fear.'

- Ventasta the Glimpser

ACT III

THE SIEGE OF EXCELSIS

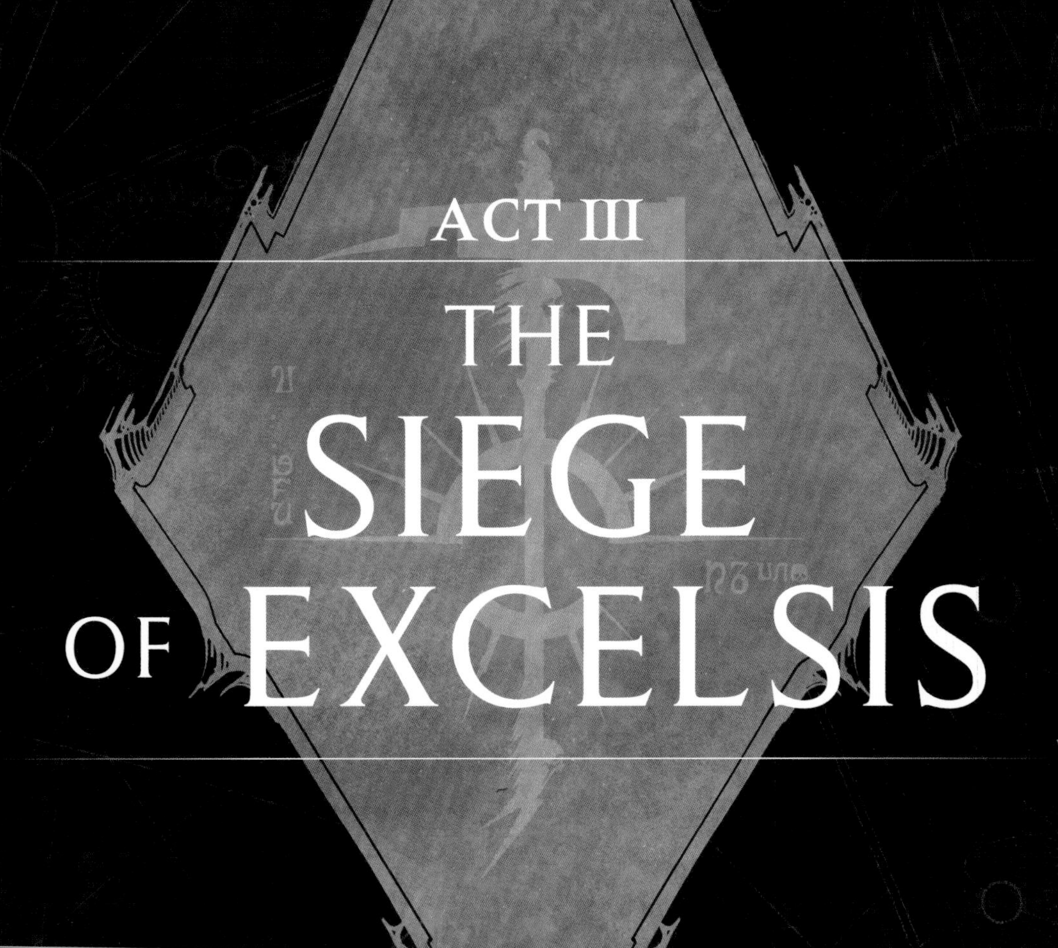

DISTANT THUNDER

Excelsis was still reeling from the suddenness of the skaven invasion when the banners of Gordrakk's horde appeared on the horizon. The city's defenders were already stretched, and with their navy halved at a stroke, the metropolis's claims of strength were paper-thin. Only in unity could it possibly hope to survive.

Those meagre preparations that the Grand Conclave had ordered to be put in place in light of the rumours of an oncoming orruk Waaagh! had been abandoned, sidetracked or even sabotaged as the turmoil of the last few months grew to a head. The city, still at war with itself over whether the use of magic was a godly act, tried to concentrate on multiple things at once – and hence ended up doing none of them. With the Tzeentchian invasion in living memory, it would have been easy to imagine the city pulling together in the face of the coming adversity, but in most of the city's districts, quite the opposite was true. Excelsis was swiftly falling apart.

In places, the better side of human nature saw people working together for each other's benefit. In the long weeks since the night of the skaven uprising, human bucket chains had relayed seawater from the harbour to the worst affected zones. Everything from soup tureens to wheelbarrows to the wax-sealed craniums of long-dead gargants were used as receptacles in the ongoing fight to keep the blazes at bay. Gate taxation doubled, then tripled, until merchants and traders were bled white; added to the proceeds of exported glimmerings mined at a frantic pace, the city brought in as much wealth as it could muster. Yet the coffers were emptied almost as soon as they were filled, spent on the employment of duardin earthworkers to dot the grounds outside the walls with mobile artillery emplacements, Kharadron fleets to patrol the skies, and mercenaries of a hundred different stripes.

Amongst the privateers who usually plied the Coast of Tusks were barbarian warriors from Lendu and Bjarl, Fyreslayers from Blazeroarer Isle across the Clawing Sea, and even a trio of Shyishan Necromancers who claimed to have renounced Nagash's dictats to better study the resurrection of monstrous beasts. When a hundreds-strong company of ogor sellswords made harbour from the south, claiming to have heard of Excelsis's plight and being more than happy to take advantage of it, the paymasters of the city made haste to strike a deal. In exchange for each ogor receiving a barrel of meat and ale every day, they would fight back the orruks in the event of a breach of the city walls. The paymasters pushed their luck somewhat by combining food and drink in the same barrel, but the result was so delicious that the ogors let it slide.

The Knights Excelsior were never still. Working in concert with the Order of Azyr and the more hard-line Freeguild companies, they tirelessly hunted down the last of the skaven that had infiltrated the city during Rattachak's assault, incinerating their warrens in controlled burns that, whilst a stalwart defence against corruption, only added to the palls of smoke wreathing the city. Meanwhile, their Lord-Castellants assisted in fortifying the city's walls, draping the most well-defended towers and strongpoints with banners that depicted grimacing gargoyles and armoured griffons – images that might intimidate a normal foe but would act as a red rag to a raging bull in the orruk psyche. Earthworks, spiked punji pits and even transplanted copses of trees ensured that the ground outside the city would funnel the invaders into carefully prepared killing fields, and the training grounds echoed day and night to the sounds of musket and cannon fire. Many a house in the Veins was turned into a sniper's nest or an ammunition store, bridges over alleyways were remade to include murder holes, and household stairs were rigged to hold the weight of a human but collapse into a pantry full of stakes should an orruk try to gain them. Every man, woman and child over the age of ten was expected to fight to the death if needed, and with the vast majority of the citizens being of Ghurish stock, there were very few who sought to shirk this duty.

Where the aelves went out in daylight, they did so in strength, for a single aelf abroad in Excelsis was all but an incitement to riot. Word had spread throughout the various aelven subcultures about the city turning upon them, and with Wanderers and Order Serpentis agents forsaking the city as well as Privateers, the metropolis lost much of its awareness of events unfolding across the wider Heartlands. Only the Darkling Covens stayed behind in any measure of force, for their Sorceress rulers had invested heavily in the forbidding spire of the Citadel Tenebris. Even that darksome tower found itself assailed by chanting mobs at times. When rumours reached the city that Morathi had taken Anvilgard in Aqshy by using her influence over the Darkling Covens to pull a massive military coup, the hostility became even more overt, and even the threat of greenskin invasion could not quell it. It looked very much like the Citadel Tenebris would become subject to a siege within a siege.

The city's defences were by no means limited to the physical. Operating under armed guard, the Collegiate Arcane had gone to great lengths to enchant the main gates, placing runes of sanctity and strength across every stanchion and length of lumber involved in their reinforcement. All agreed that if the orruks were to concentrate their assault anywhere, it would be there, and the Vanguard riders of the Astral Templars had spoken not only of entire families of lumbering gargants among the greenskin horde but also of a battering ram of surpassing size that could break even a Stormkeep into rubble. Potent enchantments were inscribed on cannonballs and Helstorm rockets, thrice-blessed bullets were handed out amongst the Freeguild and Ironweld marksmen alike, and every morning the city's plazas rang to the sound of fervent Sigmarite prayer.

It was the White Reaper, however, who had secured the city's most powerful arcane defence of all. His message, sent via the star-eagle Brightclaw through the Varantia Portal to Chamon's Spiral Crux, had reached Gardus Steel Soul of the Hallowed Knights. The Lord-Celestant had thought long on how best to communicate Sentanus' plea for arcane reinforcement to the ancient being he had won to his cause in his battle against the daemon Be'lakor. He had not realised that simply meditating upon the nature of that creature opened an astral link of sorts with its consciousness, for Gardus had been marked as a fulcrum of fate in the Great Plan. The slann known as Lord Kroak appeared to him in a dream that night; though he did not speak, he left him in no doubt that his message was received and that it was of the gravest importance that the course of fate be altered. An ancient nemesis had been freed, and though the slann's own magic had held it at bay for aeons, that time was over. Soon, the only option would be to confront it head on. Worse still, the slann's divinations had revealed a brand new threat to the Mortal Realms making its play for Excelsis, a hidden canker at the heart of the Crystalfall. There was not time enough to muster the Seraphon from Mekitopsar; Lord Kroak would have to intervene directly for the first time in many, many years.

As the banners of the greenskin hordes appeared on the horizon, the embassy of the Seraphon in Excelsis was lit by a blaze of crackling celestial energy. From nowhere, Lord Kroak appeared above the Serpentanis, and though he came alone, there was much excitement amongst the humble skinks of that mysterious pyramid. Hidden by his own enchantments and the shielding magic of his palanquin, Kroak remained anonymous and invisible to the city at large, secretly placing his own runes of protection on the city gates and working subtle geomantic spells to calm the land for the mayhem to come. The sudden clangour of celebration in Serpentanis was remarked upon only as idle gossip by its neighbours. None paid it much heed – none, at least, save Doralia ven Denst.

Returning to the pyramid in the dead of night, Doralia sought the counsel of the same Starpriest that had imparted its visions to her during her last visit. It reassured her that a great and beneficent force had arrived in the city, and that all would be well; preparation rather than exodus was key, and the coming storm would blow itself out. What it did not say was that its new master had deemed the death of Excelsis an acceptable loss, its demise a price worth paying if the End of Empires could be occupied long enough for the realmgates of the Ghurish Heartlands to be sealed by Seraphon artifice, thereby confining the destructive, vengeful god to the Realm of Beasts rather than risking it threatening Azyr.

From atop the Serpentanis embassy, Lord Kroak wields magics both subtle and devastating as he guides his Seraphon to shatter the cohesion of the orruk assault.

THE ONCOMING HORDE

The appearance of the greenskin horde on the horizon had a galvanising effect on the city's defenders. With the enemy's crude banners, totems and pennants jutting high, and their monstrous warriors looming even higher, it was clear that the enemy numbered in the tens of thousands.

Excelsis had felt the teeth of an orruk attack many times before, but never like this. Should they break through the walls – and given the miles-long size of the city's curtain wall and the raw brute strength of the savage hordes, that was a distinct possibility – they would rampage through the streets to finish what the skaven had started a few weeks previously. The sense of impending doom gave a focus to the city's defenders. Rumours that there was something evil stirring in the Crystalfall were put out of mind, as were the disturbing reports of people going missing from the parts of the city that bordered it and the glimmering-gleaned visions of hideous winged queens hatching from bejewelled chrysalises to scream triumph at a smoke-filled sky. There was simply no time to investigate, for in a matter of days, the greenskin horde would be upon them.

The Order of Azyr, having their work cut out for them keeping the city from civil war, were also highly reluctant to investigate the Crystalfall incidents in strength. There was something very unsettling about the situation, that much was true, and the recent information circulating from the ven Densts that the Nullstone Brotherhood was operating under false authority had meant even those hard-line Sigmarites were viewed askance by Galen and Doralia's fellow witch hunters. But provided the quarantine wall around the place remained intact – and it had been built by duardin masons to last centuries, if not millennia – Crystalfall was considered the lesser evil facing the city. Familiarity had pulled its teeth, and even though the citizens made the sign of the hammer as they passed it out of habit, the talk on the streets was about orruks and little else.

Amongst the smouldering ruins of the docks, all eyes were on the horizon. The Clawing Sea was ferocious, not least because of the oceanic monsters that prowled its depths, but the prospect of fighting some hideous, tentacled terror from the deep would not stop an orruk onslaught – if anything, it was likely to encourage it. Sure enough, two days after the greenskins had appeared to the west of the city in the direction of Carcass Donse, a ramshackle assemblage of masts flying the tusked skull hove into view. It was not a navy so much as a repurposed collection of shipwrecks, badly strapped together and with ramshackle trebuchets in place of cannons and ballistae. To the famous fleetmaster Arika Zenthe and her fellow aelven privateers, it would have been laughable. But Zenthe and her fellows had long abandoned that stretch of coast. Though the indigenous sea monsters claimed a good third of the rafts in explosions of timber, blood and brief displays of violence, the orruks and grots riding steadily towards Excelsis came on without pause. In the dockyards, burnt-out buildings were taken apart for what little sound lumber could be salvaged and turned into barricades, rough palisades and crow's nest shooting galleries, but the mood was sombre, for any determined greenskin assault would burst right through them.

The orruks approaching on foot would be attacking one of Sigmar's capital fortress-cities, reinforced for a hundred years against the bestial attacks of Ghur and manned from end to end by well-prepared soldiers and determined city folk who were no strangers to war. Many were the children of the Reclaimed, those who had fought tooth and nail against the scourge of Chaos and lived to tell the tale. And they were not armed with the rudimentary weapons so common to the Ghurish tribes; with the city's wealth having blossomed since the trade of glimmerings was mastered, the defenders had guns, muskets, cannons, Helstorm Rocket Batteries and even a number of Steam Tanks with which to fight their cause. The walls bristled with firepower enough to make a Greywater gun-sergeant nod with approval.

The mood amongst the citizenry was stern, but there was an undercurrent of optimism. The orruks were a foe they could understand; after fighting the mutating, twisted scions of Chaos and the scourge of the incorporeal Nighthaunt in the wake of Nagash's thrice-cursed Necroquake, the idea of fighting a foe whose principal asset was brute strength seemed almost a relief. The drill sergeants and Lord-Castellants put about the rumour that though the horde fast crossing the leagues towards the city was

massive, it was neither as large as it could have been nor as large as the prophecies surmised. They had every chance of victory – and in believing it, the city's defenders made it more likely to be correct.

It was Lord-Castellant Meloria Evenblade who called the first shot, the light of her lantern blazing from the taller of the asymmetrical spires atop the Master Gatehouse. As one, half a hundred cannons answered her call. Their designated target was not the massed horde but whatever giants wandered amongst it, for they were the biggest threat to the city's walls. First to fit that description was the pack of lumbering, misshapen monsters at the front line, ambling forward with a slow but unstoppable momentum. They were not gargants, as they had appeared at such a distance, but a troggherd, with several Dankhold Troggoths looming at the fore. The cannonade blasted several of the creatures bodily apart and ripped limbs from dozens more in sprays of foul, black blood. Yet there was a reason Skragrott and Gordrakk had chosen the dull-witted beasts to lead the advance. Where ogors or even gargants would have broken at the sheer devastation of that opening volley, the troggoths kept lumbering forward, looking quizzically at their severed limbs before once more setting their sunken red eyes on the city walls. Their very stupidity was their shield – that, and the fact that many of their number regenerated their wounds in a display of gruesome, grisly resilience, their torn guts healing over and their missing limbs sprouting anew. By the time Meloria and her gunners realised that their shots were better spent elsewhere, the horde had gained another half a mile, the thunder of their drums gradually joined by the low, guttural roar of a gathering Waaagh!.

Gradually resolving in the dust clouds beyond the front lines was a huge, interlocking set of mantlets made of sharpened galewood trees, each trunk the width of a man's waist. Meloria Evenblade squinted as she made out what they were – the former palisade walls of frontier towns, flattened en route to Excelsis and repurposed as shields. Such huge defensive structures could never have been wielded by mortal men, but they were carried to war by gargants, some of which were so large that their lesser kindred came up only to their waists. Amongst this walking, wooden fortress was something that made Evenblade's lip curl and her guts twist: a colossal battering ram carried by a dozen lesser gargants, the massive, bull-like skull at its head glowering from empty sockets each the size of caves. It was the cranium of a godbeast, that much was clear, and such epic monstrosities had a powerful magic all to themselves. Here was the greenskin horde's intent writ large – not to scale the walls but to smash them down.

THE SEVEN TOWERS BESIEGED

The people of Ghur had long learnt how to erect effective defences against monstrous foes, and the seven towers upon which their curtain wall was built bristled with spiked palisades, artillery platforms and reinforced gates. Yet here that immovable object was to meet the irresistible force of a full scale Waaagh!.

Excelsis's western gate, long ago built up as the main entrance to the city, was dominated by a massive gatehouse tower and flanked by three more on each side. From the tall, asymmetrical spires that capped the Westgate Tower, Lord-Castellant Evenblade of the Knights Excelsior coordinated the city's defence. With a fierce shout and a wave of her lantern-stave, she gave the order for the cannons mounted upon each of the main wall's seven towers to switch targets to the greater mass of the horde and the gargants now lumbering into view behind. The troggoths were absorbing too much of their firepower for too little in the way of results. Now that it was clear that they had been shielding a greater threat, she sent one runner to the Ironweld strongpoint of the Gauntlet – the area beyond the main gates that the city's engineers had turned into a killing field – and seven more to leading members of the Collegiate Arcane, stationed atop the seven towers to avoid the stranglers and burners of the Nullstone Brotherhood who still roamed the poor rookeries of the Veins below.

Within minutes, the Gyrocopters and bombers of the city's sky battalions had taken flight en masse, their advance covered by low-hanging clouds conjured by the Collegiate wizards' tower-mounted Hurricanums. To sally forth on foot or on horseback was to court certain death, for the foe blackened the horizon, but with the greenskin horde having nothing in the way of aerial assets, the Ironweld squadrons had a

chance. Sure enough, just as Evenblade had hoped, when the airborne vanguard opened fire upon the troggherd and dropped their whirling, explosive bombshells amongst them, the beasts' advance came to a stumbling halt. The troggoths, too distracted by the buzzing, stinging flying machines to do anything but swat futilely in their direction, held up the advance of the gargants and their colossal battering ram, ambling about and generally getting in the way. Meanwhile the orruk mobs that formed the flanks flowed around them and, despite the angry roaring of their Warbosses, spread out once more to leave the gargantuan vanguard stranded behind.

For a time, it seemed as though the gyro-squadrons would unleash their payload and return without loss. Then one of them was hit by a hurled boulder the size of a hay bale; the duardin pilot veered as he flew but not quickly enough. Spinning wildly out of control, the Gyrocopter wheeled down into the massed ranks of the orruks and grots below, killing scores of the greenskins to the amusement of those behind. Another craft was hit, then another, as the gargants behind their mantlet-carrying kin picked up on the idea, filling the air with chunks of debris, fallen masonry – even the ribs of dead monsters, which the oafs hurled like clumsy boomerangs at the swooping Gyrocopters. Led by a cherry-red craft with an impressive array of guns, known to Evenblade as the Scarlet Scourge, the squadron regrouped half a mile away from the gargants at the centre of the horde, flying as high as they could to avoid retribution. Moments later, they realised they had chosen their site poorly when one of the ambling, squat-bodied Maw-krushas among the armoured orruks leapt impossibly high for its size, swiping out a claw to catch one Gyrocopter as its rider sunk his axes into the hull of the Scarlet Scourge. The booming laugh of Gordrakk echoed over the horde's dull roar, for it was none other than the Fist of Gork, riding atop Bigteef, the creature's deep scars and battered skull still an ugly red after its titanic fight in Carcass Donse. He hacked at the Scarlet Scourge's rotor engine with one axe and hung grimly onto its fuselage with the other as it spiralled into the ground. The impact crater burning around him, Gordrakk hauled out the bloody remains of the pilot to bite deep into his head, ripping it clean from his neck in a spray of gore. The surviving aircraft hauled off and made for the cover of the low-lying clouds, the jeers of greenskins ringing in their ears.

With daunting inevitability, a vast mass of orruks had come close enough for the long-rifle handgunners on the walls to open fire. They concentrated their shots on the leaders, bullseyeing several with each passing minute to send them tumbling into the muck, but, by this point, there was little need for leadership in the greater orruk psyche. Now that they were within spitting distance of a good scrap, there was no stopping them, and the din of their war cries was deafening. The Waaagh! itself was a sonic assault that drowned out the orders and clarions of the gun line atop the battlements of the seven towers even as it empowered the gibbering, green-eyed shamans vomiting gouts of primal magic below. The largest gargants were flinging boulders as high and as far as they could, each landing with a colossal impact to shatter a swathe of rampart or crush a line of blackpowder gunners packed in too tightly atop the walls to evade.

Most of the artillery were now concentrating their firepower on the vast, bull-headed battering ram that approached the main gates. Propelled by a dozen lesser gargants on either side and a hulking Warstomper bellowing invective as it pushed from the rear, the great wheeled monstrosity was gathering speed. Lord-Castellant Evenblade gave the order to thicken fire on the battering ram, and many a solid hit was landed, but the gargants simply kicked their wounded kindred aside, dropped their palisade mantlets and broke into a lumbering, loping run with the weight of Hammergord hefted between them. Those cannonballs that struck the battering ram itself may as well have been aimed at a cliff face, for the petrified bone was inherently magical and could not be undone by mere physical attacks. Those that hit the gargants, along with stinging, flesh-ripping volleys of handgun bullets, were for the most part shrugged off. The raw greenskin energy of the Waaagh! was coursing through the horde around them, and the giants were invigorated by it, drunk on it, intoxicated to the point that all they cared about was wreaking utter destruction.

Only when the battering ram was a hundred metres from the gates did Gordrakk thunder alongside it on Bigteef, leaping at the last to stand astride the mighty skull of Hammergord and raise his axes high in the air. Then the ram struck the rune-inscribed gates of Excelsis with the force of two dozen gargants behind it. The runes flared, those traced upon it by Lord Kroak burning bright enough to blind.

With an ear-splitting crack, the skull of Hammergord shattered into a thousand pieces.

THE SHATTERING BLOW

The walls of Excelsis had been tested, not by a simple siege but by the stone-pulverising power of a titanic magical relic. Still they stood proud. But the rulers of the greenskin hordes had suspected that it would not be so easy, and their true strength was yet to be unleashed...

The siege had been a straight punch from a gnarled and armoured fist. Gordrakk knew his warriors well enough to realise that a protracted campaign of starvation was out of the question; with the city in sight, it would be no time at all before some aspiring Warboss led a charge of his own. And when one section of his horde charged, the rest would follow.

Skragrott had convinced Gordrakk to let the troggherd under Glogg lead the assault to soak up the most part of the human city's artillery fire, and the cunning grot still had a few aces to play. But Gordrakk's strategy was a simple one, as it always had been – charge Hammergord straight for the city gates and smash them to matchwood. Unfortunately, the city had been more than prepared for it. Now Gordrakk lay out cold on the battlements of the Westgate Tower, flung there by the arcane explosion that had destroyed the godbeast skull he had ridden to the gates. He had levelled a frontal assault and paid the price.

The city's Freeguild defenders had initially scrabbled away in horror when Gordrakk's body had sailed over the crenellated wall to crash down hard on the flagstones, one arm twisted at a weird angle and gore smeared across his face. Now, as the warlord lay there prone, they moved in, swords drawn, in search of an easy victory. One of the braver souls took a stab at his exposed waist with a halberd, but still the fallen warlord did not move. Could the grand leader of the orruk horde already be dead?

Now the Excelsians began to take their toll in earnest. With the battering ram shattered to pieces and the gargants that had manned it reeling back in disarray, the gunners of the seven towers sent forth a deadly fusillade every few seconds. Boiling tar, imported Aqshian vitriol and heated lead was spewed from gargoyle-spouts and poured through murder holes wherever the walls overhung the bawling orruks below. As the Mega-Gargants waded through the press, intent on ripping the walls to pieces with their bare hands or battering them down with enormous clubs and flails, they were met by salvos of Helstorm rockets that blinded and disoriented them. Gorko the Big was shot by three cannonballs in quick succession, a volley that sent him crashing down to squash half a dozen armoured orruks under his colossal weight. Droon the Towerer took a Knight-Venator's arrow to his eye, reeling back before staggering away to find easier prey. There was simply no subtlety to the Mega-Gargants' attack, and with the artillery of the seven towers able to spot their assault from so far away, there was time enough to calibrate for maximum effect. Every time one of the behemoths fell, there was a great shout of jubilation from the ramparts, for their position on the walls grew considerably safer with the death of each lumbering monstrosity.

At the Westgate Tower, a deafening bellow tore through the air, the battlements toppling in a rumble of shattering stone as the Maw-krusha Bigteef hauled its ten-ton bulk over the parapet. It opened its jaws wide and gave another mind-numbing roar. The halberdiers screamed in agony, toppling back with blood trickling from their noses, ears and mouths. Gordrakk winced, sat up, and then sprang to his feet, his ensorcelled choppas hacking down the reeling humans around him with brutal efficiency. He heard a low growl and turned to stare daggers at Bigteef just as it was about to bite him in half. The creature had been even more bad-tempered than usual since Kragnos had beat it bloody in the chasm of Donse. It locked eyes with Gordrakk for a long moment before offering its haunches to its old master. Gordrakk flung back his head and gave vent to a full-throated war cry, which was answered not only by the din of ten thousand orruks outside the city but also by a deep bass rumble that many Excelsians took for thunder. Was this the vengeance of Sigmar, borne on the tempest?

Then, bursting from the rocky spires to the south-east, something massive hove into view that turned the defenders' hope to plunging despair. Kragnos, the End of Empires, had come. He was already at full gallop, a hundred heavily armoured orruk cavalry on snorting Gore-gruntas close behind him. His charge started some distance away but was made at an

oblique angle, curving in to align with the walls as he came in from the flank at speed. The ground cracked under his hooves, fissures forming in all directions as the steady thunder of his charge shook the earth; in response, spires toppled and badly made shanties collapsed in a swathe across Excelsis. Lord-Castellant Evenblade shouted for the towers' artillerists to open fire at will, but their guns were lined up on the looming Mega-Gargants at the walls, and only a few had the discipline to retrain their cannons and Helstorm Rocket Batteries on the new threat barrelling towards them. A trio of smoke-trailing rockets from the nearest tower arced down towards him, a volley levelled in haste but lucky enough to be on target. Two detonated on the hardened bronze of the shield Tuskbreaker. The other hit his bare chest, leaving a crater of blackened flesh. For a moment, the trailing burst of flame made Kragnos look like a living meteor – and it was with much the same impact that he hit the walls of the city.

The giant centauroid lowered his head at the last, teeth gritted and curved horns levelled. His pounding charge hit the wall so hard that an entire section slewed away, the huge chunks of masonry tumbling like a cliff face in a landslide. Turning, he shoulder-barged another massive section to rubble and then galloped parallel to the wall, keeping the Dread Mace raised so its head crashed through one crenellation after another, bowling over those sheltering behind to clear the battlements entirely. A hundred tonnes of toppling stonework followed him as he dragged his weapon along the top of the walls, smashing monolithic bricks as easily as if they were thin clay urns. At the same time, the impacts of his hooves shattered the ground at the wall's base, sending yet more masonry cascading down. The curtain wall was collapsing, and with a great roar, the Gore-grunta riders pushed their steeds up the tumbled rock and over into the city beyond. Worse still, with the artillerists focusing now on Kragnos, three of the Mega-Gargants on the north side of the assault managed to reach the city. They brought their titanic clubs and flails to bear, battering great holes in the walls before elbowing and barging each breach wider and wider. Then, as the thunder of Kragnos' assault reached a crescendo and the earthquake of his anger sent its fissures ever deeper, an entire half-mile section of the walls collapsed entirely to reveal the skaven-dug warrens that had undermined them.

Excelsis had gone from being unbreachable to being horribly vulnerable in the space of a single minute.

THE VOICE AND THE TALON

The sound of thunder shook Excelsis, coming not from the skies but through the ground. It was as if the tectonic plate of Thondia itself was trembling with fear. That sound was the signal Synessa and Dexcessa had been waiting for, their hyper-attuned senses picking up on it in an instant.

Lepidopteran wings unfurled to bathe the ballroom in shimmering light, and the headless, naked aelven corpses that hung upside down from the walls writhed as the light touched them. They swelled and burst, swarms of multicoloured butterflies pouring out to turn the air a riot of colours that offended the eye. With a winching of silvered chains, Maulgen was taken down from the hooks that kept him suspended in the rafters, Daemonettes caressing him as they snipped the fetters from his body and licked his bloodied skin. He bolted as he was set loose, his bare feet lacerated by shards of broken mirror as he ran, the sound of hideous laughter ringing in his ears.

The Heralds Luxion and Vresca trilled with glee at seeing their idols finally ready to show themselves to the world outside. They held high their magical mirror to absorb the glimmering butterflies and send them winging across the void to Slaanesh; each was born from an aelf-soul and, to the Dark Prince, they would be as the finest sweetmeats. The thunder had come, and Excelsis's great curtain wall – undermined at Synessa and Dexcessa's request by the skaven that had scattered after Rattachak's invasion – had collapsed. It was time for the city's hidden conquerors to dance amidst the flames of its demise and offer the symphony of panic and savagery to their patron god.

The abandoned ballroom had become a daemon-infested tumour in the heart of the Crystalfall, its exterior as broken as ever but its interior a sumptuous palace of the flesh. Now the horrors within burst out.

Dexcessa led the charge, sceptre outstretched and peacock wings billowing behind. The Talon tapped the quarantine wall where the seismic tremors shaking the city had left their mark, turning it to cracked glass. Synessa whispered a single word, and the vitrified wall shattered in a hurricane of shards. Up and around they whirled, a killing, razored vortex that the twins wound around themselves like a cloak.

Out into the city poured the daemon procession, Luxion and Vresca at the head with their sacred mirror borne between two blade-wheeled chariots. The scattered citizens of Excelsis fell back in horror; with virtually all those capable of holding a sword locked in the battle at the walls, there were none to stop their advance save pockets of Nuller Flagellants who had put the persecution of magic users above the defence of their own city. Such dregs did not last long against the splendour of the Newborn.

Through the Crystalfall districts they went, straight for Squallside, where the stormstone townhouses of those rich enough to buy their way out of military service rose high. Those who witnessed Dexcessa's splendour or heard Synessa's clarion oratory gawped, their souls taken by a twisted version of love at first sight, and emerged from their hiding places to join the procession. Onwards went the Talon and the Voice, their devoted Hedonite followers around them and the scattered citizenry trailing and dancing in their wake like children after a Sigmarsday piper.

When the Slaaneshi host came upon a field hospital in the Gildensquare, the medics took up sword, surgical blade and bonesaw alike, with even wounded soldiers joining the fight. But it was like trying to stop water trickling across a riverbed, and the cobbles soon ran red. As Luxion and Vresca brought their great mirror into the fray, those last few survivors who caught their reflection went mad in an instant, cutting at themselves and their fellows before dying in panicked ecstasy. Amongst it all, Synessa and Dexcessa preened, congratulating themselves on their perfect timing.

By the time the twins reached the Palace Excelsium, their carnival throng included beggars and honour guards, rich aristocrats and poor glimmermen, all artfully spattered with gore by the daemon riders that corralled them forward. With scant military forces to stop them, the way was open to the heart of the city. Their febrile court singing their praises all the while, Synessa and Dexcessa would claim the seat of its power all but unopposed, and from there, turn Kragnos and his hordes into their devoted servants.

TO STRIKE LIKE LIGHTNING

Everywhere, the city's defenders were reeling. They had been assailed not only by a savage army but also a deity of Destruction and the daemonspawn offspring of a god of Chaos. There was scant chance for victory, but whilst the Stormcast Eternals still fought, there was hope nonetheless.

The battle at the curtain wall was so intense, so deafening, that it was impossible to think, and the press of bodies was so thick that it was hard to see beyond the point of a sword. Two huge sections of the city's ramparts had tumbled, one because of Kragnos' rampage, the other through a combination of gargantuan brute force and hidden skaven cunning. Wherever the wall had become a hillock of rubble, there the orruks surged forwards – and there the defenders of the city desperately tried to hold the line. The Knights Excelsior were as a bulwark of blades, cutting down anything that tried to storm their position with ruthless precision, but their numbers were low, and they could not be everywhere at once. Where the Stormcast Eternals could not cover, bright-uniformed Freeguilders were ranked up tight, each regiment a local legend with a storied history and a great many battles under their belts. But in the face of the muscular, roaring orruks barrelling over the rubble of the breach, they seemed woefully unprepared.

The spear blocks of the Stormblessed regiment found the tips of their weapons turned aside by the rugged, finger-thick iron of the brutes that led the charge. Even when their spears sank home, the orruks would come on regardless, snapping the shafts with their bare hands and laying into the soldiery beyond with savage hooked axes. The Bronze Claws, the celebrated halberdier regiment that was the pride of Squallside,

commended their souls to Sigmar before charging to shore up the breach that Kragnos himself had wrought. They were met by an avalanche of flesh, bad temper and rusted metal as the invaders' Gore-grunta cavalry stormed through. The Coldguard, the city's de facto law enforcers in times of prosperity, stood in the path of a howling tribe of near-naked orruk savages. Though the Freeguilders took a heavy toll, they found their swordwork all but useless against the insensate frenzy of the leader, Gulgaz Stoneklaw. Tongue lolling, shrunken heads bobbing at his shoulders, the orruk Big Boss took a whole host of wounds and still did not fall. His chompa hacked into the defenders again and again until he broke the Coldguard lines single-handedly. The remnants of his tribe were quick to follow up and ran yelling into the streets.

Suddenly, the skies split, a searing light flared, and the angels of Sigmar stepped from nothingness to blitz the orruk line as one.

In the space of a heartbeat, the deep burgundy armour of the Astral Templars now shone alongside the blood-spattered white of the Knights Excelsior. The newcomers were clad in fur as much as plate, their tattooed faces bright with battlelust and their voices raised in raucous song. Wherever an orruk leader loomed out of the horde, a bearded Paladin would vault over the rubble to take them on in single combat. When a towering gargant pushed its way through the breach, shouldering aside the shattered masonry, an Astral Templar would run along the broken battlements, war cry rising over the cacophony of battle, leaping and landing atop the giant's shoulders to hack at its neck.

Lightning struck the Westgate Tower, and Gordrakk himself was assailed by four armoured Stormcasts. Long-hafted blades thrust in close to be turned aside at the last second by his choppas. They worked to surround him, keeping him off balance, and he found he was suddenly fighting for his life. Then Bigteef crushed two of them into blurs of arcane energy with thumping blows of its massive, scaly fists. Laughing gutturally, the Fist of Gork made good on the opening by leaping forward and body-slamming the leader of the Stormcast strike force over the shattered crenellations, sending him plunging forty feet into the throng below. A flash of lightning glinted in the orruk warlord's eye as he turned on the last remaining Templar. There was a resounding clang of blades, and the skirmish ended in a scream and a blaze of cerulean energy.

Already the battle outside the walls was turning into a bloodbath. Spearheads of Astral Templars were counter-attacking with headlong, bellicose force to hack their way through the throng, always aiming for the largest, most intimidating targets. Six gargants were cut down, though it took the most part of an entire Warrior chamber to do it. A pair of Maw-krushas thumping through the press met their match in Lord-Celestant Darrakos and his Stardrake Andromandus, the celestial beast baiting them and leading them away from Excelsis with such skill that they crushed scores of orruks and bowled over dozens of mantlets in their haste to clamp their jaws on its scaly hide.

The massive, barnacle-encrusted Dankhold Troggoth known as Glogg was surrounded, its legs having been hacked away at the knees by greataxes limned with celestial energy, but it fought on nonetheless, swinging its stalactite club and roaring in anger to take half a dozen Astral Templars down in as many seconds. A blaze of lightning from a levitating Lord-Arcanum withered the troggoth's arm to nothing; reeling in shock, Glogg returned fire with a hissing torrent of vomit that burnt the mage's flesh to the bone. Eight more Stormcasts, three Dracoths and a Gryph-hound were killed by the mighty Glogg before it finally succumbed to its wounds, but succumb it did, its head sliced from its neck even as the few surviving Templars were overwhelmed by the teeming orruks all around them.

Even on the bay around the Spear of Mallus, battle raged. The ramshackle flotilla of orruk vessels were finally making landfall – at least, what was left of them, for the Angelos conclaves of the Knights Excelsior, in conjunction with the sea monsters prowling the bay, had taken a grievous toll on the would-be naval invasion. Swift enough to avoid the catapult-style artillery aimed hastily in defence, the Astral Templars' vanguard riders rode the scree and sand of the bay, their throwing axes and zigzag blades taking the heads from those orruks scrambling through the surf towards the city. Then a large wave broke against the shore, followed by another. It was the third that brought the harbour's doom.

A score of massive Kraken-eater Mega-Gargants rose like titans of legend from the waves, each wearing the remnants of shattered rafts and galleons as mantles, flotsam with which they had disguised themselves as they had waded along the sea bed to approach unseen. The Astral Templars roared in jubilation; here was a fight that would resonate across the aeons. The Knights Excelsior, however, remained silent. With the defences of the harbour whittled down to almost nothing, there was no way they could stop the seaborne assault from causing utter destruction in the city beyond.

GODS AND MONSTERS

As the battle raged on into night, it was becoming clear that the intervention of the Stormcast Eternals would not be enough. At the breaches, at the harbour, even from the tunnels below the city, greenskins were breaking through to run pell-mell through the streets. Excelsis's lifespan could be measured in hours at most.

At the boundaries of the city, the streets were seething with greenskin bodies. The great god Kragnos had smashed his way along the wall, crushing great sections of it with Dread Mace and fell hoof before he reached the gate itself. Already he had broken the city's perimeter, and his Mega-Gargants had done much the same job at the north wall and harbour alike. But there was a statement to be made, and that Kragnos understood more than most. Standing tall before the gate, he reared high like a bucking stallion, handgunners and rocketsmen firing desperately at his torso to no more effect than a swarm of stinging hornets. For a moment, the Drogrukh deity was silhouetted against the setting sun, then he brought both forefeet down upon the gate at once, slamming his mace between them at the same time.

With a terrific bang, the colossal impacts overloaded the runic protections and split the gate into three pieces that span away into the streets, scything through the melee of men and orruks before crashing into the merchant buildings beyond. Kragnos muscled his way through the twisted iron hinges. A score of Astral Templars were sprinting right for him, their grins of fierce battlelust wide behind their impassive helms. Incensed such insects should challenge him, Kragnos gave vent to a roar of outrage, bowling the Templars backwards even as he stamped his hooves to crumble the earth beneath them. The Stormcasts fell into the rubble-strewn passageways under the city, betrayed by the collapsing paving stones as Kragnos leapt straight over them and pounded at full gallop through the melee.

At the northernmost section of the curtain wall, the body of Warstomper Gronk blocked the breach. His fate had been death by a thousand cuts, for the arrows of a Justicar conclave's archers had poured into his torso and face while their sword-wielding brethren had hacked at his legs from the street below. His colossal bulk formed a wall of flesh, stemming the tide of orruks that had been clambering through. Only the skittering Grimscuttle tribes that picked over the rubble on dexterous arachnid mounts made it through to assail the white-armoured Liberators barricading the streets, their attack bolstered by black-robed grots that teemed from the undermined tunnels. With the Freeguild regiments locked in battle at the towers, a company of Excelsian ogor mercenaries held the flank, squashing grots with every blow of their metal-banded clubs.

Then the unthinkable happened. From the tunnels came Skragrott, his moon-staff held high and his crown of boss-fungus glowing sickly green as the Bad Moon leered out from behind the clouds. The grots shrieked in glee, renewing their attack in a frenzy. The Loonking gave a long, ululating shout, and the ogors turned their violent attentions from the greenskins to the Knights Excelsior. The shieldwall of the Liberators, so efficacious a barrier against the grots, was smashed apart in short order by the raging ogor turncoats as tendrils of glowing green magic from Skragrott's staff wrenched Judicators from their sniper's nests and dashed them down into the streets below. In a single, gut-wrenching turn of fate, the northern wall had fallen.

As the thick evening mists rolled into the harbour, the air was turned blue by Derko Walrusbiter's coarse insults as he stamped flat those dockside taverns and inns that the skaven invasion had not put to the torch. He laid about himself with a huge, rubbery tentacle ripped from the Terror of Izalend some months before, pausing only to scoop up barrels of ale from cobwebbed basements or squish those citizens paralysed with fear by the appearance of a titanic monster dripping with brine. With Derko were half a dozen other Kraken-eaters sent by Skragrott to make the coastal assault; they had simply stepped over the Astral Templars who had sought to stop them, their beady eyes fixed on the bounty of the city beyond. Those orruks that had made it all the way into the harbour splashed through the surf and sprinted, invigorated by the scent of war, to charge pell-mell at the Stormcasts instead.

Derko turned as he felt something sting his neck, then something else stabbed at the base of his spine. It took a moment for the pain to register, but when it did, he roared in the white heat of an agony he had never felt before. Next to him, Grottob the Gullet fell hard to crush a dockside temple to dust. Long Dobb was next to go down, a score of long, steel shafts dripping some vile green liquid sprouting from his broad back like the quills of a porcupine.

From the mists of the harbour, a hundred tall ships emerged into view. Most were sleek black wolfships bearing the insignia of the Scourge Privateers, but at their head was a massive vessel the size of an island, a Black Ark with a skull-like prow and a multitude of sails. Coming about as they entered the bay, the ships sent volley after volley of long, poisoned harpoons whistling through the evening air to thunk into the bare flesh of Derko and his fellow Mega-Gargants.

With a great roar of defiance, Derko splashed back out into the surf, diving headlong into the water to send a double wave crashing outwards. Harpoons punctured the surface, but he had dived deep into the bay, leaving his few remaining Kraken-eaters in the harbour to take the brunt of the fleet's firepower instead. A few tense moments later, Derko roared back out of the water in the shadow of the Spear of Mallus to grab hold of the Black Ark's prow, snapping off the tip of its figurehead and using it to smash the front of the giant ship to flinders.

Shadows curled from the Black Ark's forecastle, a set of giant wings and a serpentine body discernible amongst them. Derko swiped his cable-thewed arms at the apparition, but it was like fighting smoke. Only once the coils of shadow had wrapped around his torso and head like those of a constrictor-snake did they coalesce, tightening and becoming steel-hard as they twisted this way and that. With a great shout of triumph, the shadow goddess took full and glorious form, her coils ripping Derko's massive head from his neck in a gouting fountain of blood.

It took scant minutes for that dark-sailed fleet to make dock, for Fleetmaster Zenthe had briefed the captains well of the harbour's ways, and they acted in swift efficiency as only aelven sailors can. Hundreds of sleek, lithe Witch Aelves debarked down long ramps of blackwood, then hundreds more, gladiatrices and athletes of war vaulting through the white mounds of shellfish-scree to leap straight into the dockside melee. Trapped between the unforgiving wall of sigmarite that was the Astral Templars defence and the hurricane of blades that was the aelven onslaught, the battered greenskin navy was cut to pieces. Soon the surf ran red, carrion seabirds picking at the corpses of dead Kraken-eaters and lacerated orruks as they were slowly claimed by the Clawing Sea.

Morathi-Khaine had come, and from the darkest quarter, Excelsis had been given hope anew.

THE CITY'S DARK HEART

Great swathes of orruks had bullied their way past the outer defences and were running amok in the city. Some were gunned down in well-prepared kill zones and others fell through false grates or trapped stairways, yet always there were more.

Only when the faithful of Morathi-Khaine joined the fight in the city streets did the orruks truly find themselves outclassed. Here the cumulative psychological drive of the Waaagh! was diminished; with the orruks forced to split into smaller groups to negotiate the narrow streets, shanties and alleyways, the tidal wave of their onslaught was broken into streams. It was just as Lord Kroak had foreseen: to meet the foe at the gates of order would have been to waste what strength they had and inflame the bestial soul to boot. No, to break the green wave's power, it would first have to lose its momentum and then be dashed apart on the rocks of civilisation.

And here, in the labyrinth of streets and shadows, was where the Daughters of Khaine truly excelled. Darting from slanted roofs they came, dancing over piled corpses and laughing as their knives slit throats to the bone, every cut delivered with pinpoint expertise. The orruks fought back hard, their brute strength carrying them far, but as day turned to night, they found their momentum waning. Too late they realised that they had blundered into the den of a subtler kind of hunter. After months of persecuting the aelves as the source of all their woes, the citizens of Excelsis were grateful indeed that their strange, lethal allies had not forsaken them entirely. Through it all came the duality that was Morathi-Khaine, a towering monster and svelte queen at once, both forms exulting in her power as a goddess. When an orruk leader roared his challenge and ran towards her, axes raised, her sorceress incarnation choked him with living shadow before pulling all the blood from his body with a beckoning finger. Where a riderless Maw-krusha barrelled through the streets, her monstrous embodiment stung it in the eye with a strike of her scorpion tail before slamming it senseless into a statue of Sigmar. There was nothing that could match her – nothing, that is, save another god.

As the streets descended into mayhem around them, Galen and Doralia fought their way towards the canker at Excelsis's heart. With them came the White Reaper, for he too had seen the dire cavalcade of Slaaneshi daemons from afar and felt a great disquiet that only tackling them in person would diminish. Together they plunged along passages consumed with purple-black fire, shot their way through roving packs of archer-assassins mounted on daemon steeds, and covered their ears against the siren song of the Heralds that beckoned them to a blissful death. At the threshold of the Palace Excelsium, the ven Densts, bloodied and near exhaustion, reloaded and commended their souls to Sigmar as the White Reaper stood sentinel over them. A chorus of screams split the air; these were not cries of war, insisted Sentanus, but of torture. A prayer to the God-King on their lips, they ventured inside.

The palace floor was littered with corpses and dismembered limbs. Some repugnant agency had paired the cadavers together as if at a dance, though often they were headless or had their intestines draped around their necks like feather boas. At the centre of the tableau was the corpse of a seven-foot-tall, shaven-headed priest that Galen recognised as Maulgen, flayed from the neck down and with his mouth stuffed full to breaking point with razored shards of nullstone. Lesser souls would have lost their nerve – or at least the contents of their stomachs – but the ven Densts and their Stormcast ally strode on, grim-faced, towards the distant sound of screams.

The trio entered the Conclave Hall to see that battle still raged in the palace's heart. The Grand Matriarch Yarga-Sjuhan was jerking like a marionette atop the enormous oval table around which the city's dignitaries made their laws, her all-female honour guard dancing around her with their runic greatswords held high as if about to strike their mistress. Before her was a giant, winged demigod so beautiful and awful it hurt to look at it, twitching a delicate claw above the warriors as if puppeteering them with invisible strings. Another expansively winged daemon was at the far end of the table, tearing down a tapestry depicting the aelven pantheon's victory over the Dark Prince Slaanesh. Around them pranced and trilled an adoring throng of Daemonettes that leered and laughed at their prey.

Galen and Doralia levelled their weapons, sending nullstone bullet and rune-inscribed stake hurtling across the room to strike the daemon giants in their backs. They turned as one, faces twisted into snarls – and in that moment, the spell upon Yarga-Sjuhan and her warriors was broken. At a roared command from the Grand Matriarch, they broke apart their amberbone necklaces, instantly growing more animalistic as the realmstone's magic unleashed the beast within. Frenzied, they launched a blistering attack at Synessa, greatblades hacking into delicate limbs as the winged daemon screeched in indignation. Cerrus Sentanus bellowed, charging forwards to smite the nearest Daemonette with his sword even as his lantern-stave burnt another to strings of dissipating ichor.

At the far end of the table, Dexcessa shot forwards, claws outstretched and sceptre flashing in the light. The daemon moved too fast to follow, pulling apart the honour guard with long-nailed hands as if plucking flesh from a well-cooked game bird. Synessa gave vent to a cry, plaintive and beautiful, and a broken mirror shimmered into existence, carried towards Sentanus by a giant, half-real hand with talons like glaives. A moment before its magic took him, Doralia took careful aim and fired, shattering the spell into a thousand glass serpents that slithered away into the dark recesses of the room. Sentanus leapt atop the conclave table, sweeping Yarga-Sjuhan aside as Dexcessa's sceptre descended to crush her head and blocking the blow with his stave. The two duelled. Faster and faster their weapons clashed, the White Reaper off balance but holding his own against the far larger foe. Dexcessa laughed, wild and evil – and with a long claw, ripped Sentanus' arm from his socket in a spray of gore. Another claw pierced his throat and another his heart. It was then that the Reaper shoved his lantern-stave into the shrieking daemon's gullet and roared the words of banishment his order had kept sacred since the Age of Chaos. The exorcising light of Sigmar burst from the creature's maw, blazing from its eyes and flaring nostrils even as Sentanus died shuddering on its talons. There was an explosion of lightning, and the two disappeared without trace.

Grim but determined, Galen fired shot after nullstone shot at Synessa. The creature screeched with each bullet that marred its muscled frame, for the anti-thaumic substance was anathema to a being from beyond the realms. Turning, the Voice hurtled towards the ven Densts, painted claws extended. The ven Densts stood their ground, Doralia levelling her crossbow as her father put a bullet in the creature's eye. There was a dull twang, and a stake lodged in the recoiling daemon's chest – a stake with the name 'Sigmar Unberogen' carefully etched upon it in finest celestium. With a scream, Synessa burst apart into a thousand butterflies and was gone.

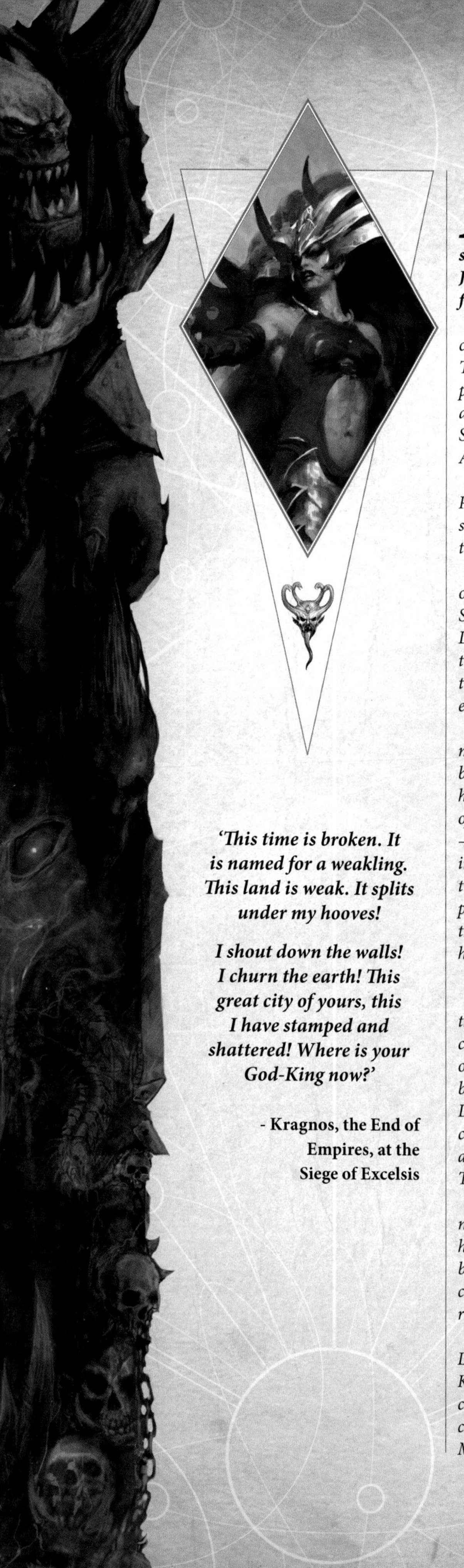

Morathi-Khaine walked slowly, steadily, towards the city's doom. Around her, throngs of wild-eyed citizens rushed past in a screaming tide, but, on some instinctual level, the crowd stayed well out of her way. Even humans can tell a goddess, she thought. Just as well, for she could turn them to scattering smoke with a flick of a fingernail. Sea voyages always made her irritable.

She turned down Mallus Broadstreet, boot heels clicking on ash-covered flagstones that trembled and split as if hammered from below. There was something sickly sweet on the breeze under the stench of human panic and burning buildings. She frowned and stopped for a moment, analysing it. A perfume of sorts drifting from the Palace Excelsium. Something she recognised, in the back of her mind. Something close. Almost... familial.

The scent was buried by a terrific, earthy stink as she crossed the Grand Plaza. There he was – a giant, roaring monstrosity in the middle distance, stamping and rearing like a bucking stallion to destroy the densely packed townhouses of Squallside in an orgy of destruction.

Kragnos, he was called. Over a thousand years before, during the Age of Myth, she had learnt of his rampage against the ancient drakes of Ghur. She had seen the Lenduan Frescoes in person, even visited the ruins of the Draconith empire during the dawn of Sigmar's civilisation, for the sorry tale had stuck with her. It was the story of a mutual, needless destruction of two nations, and its agent was here in the flesh. The god-thing was a living earthquake, and right at this moment, Excelsis was his prey.

The centauroid god felt her gaze upon him. He twisted his shaggy, maned head towards her, an expression of indignant rage in his eyes, and bellowed so loudly that her ears rang like bells. Twisting, he came towards her at full gallop, buildings collapsing on either side amidst a tsunami of dust and debris. She could see something in the billowing particles – or, rather, the lack of something – and focused to pierce the shroud of invisibility it wore like a cloak. It was a complex, floating machine of twisting half-circles, an orrery of stone with an ancient, mummified mage-priest at its heart. In the streets beyond it, she saw flashes of bright blue, the sinuous movement of Seraphon on the hunt as saurian warriors and horned warbeasts took the fight to the orruks.

'Ah,' said Morathi-Khaine. 'There you are. Late, as ever.'

Turning back to the charging deity, she spoke seven words of power in the tongue of ancient Ulgu. The shadows of the shaking, crumbling buildings coalesced into half-real tentacles that wrapped themselves around his limbs, only to recoil on contact as if stung. Tutting, Morathi-Khaine flicked her bloody fingers out, five lances of poisoned gore searing through the air. The Drogrukh beast raised his shield, and the lances dissipated in a cloud of crimson droplets without even hitting home. The living earthquake roared again, the sound shaking tiles from the roofs of those buildings still standing. To his right, the hovering stone orrery shimmered and became visible.

As if in response, the sky blazed bright and meteors streaked from nowhere, each searing white like a star ripped from the firmament and hurled straight at the beast Kragnos. The centaur-god raised his ancient bronze shield, and all the magic burned out of the celestial missiles as they came close. They struck the great verdigris disc as little more than porous rock to shatter on impact.

A swarm of silver-blue serpents rushed from the side streets beneath Lord Kroak, venomous fangs bared, but with a stamp of his great hoof, Kragnos opened a fissure beneath them that devoured them all before closing with a thunderous crash of rock. On came the bestial god, so close now that she could feel his heat. He raised his great mace, dwarfing Morathi-Khaine as he reared high for the killing strike.

'This time is broken. It is named for a weakling. This land is weak. It splits under my hooves!

I shout down the walls! I churn the earth! This great city of yours, this I have stamped and shattered! Where is your God-King now?'

- Kragnos, the End of Empires, at the Siege of Excelsis

Shooting out from the Dockstrasse came her counterpart, the Shadow Queen. Her monstrous incarnation struck like some immense cobra to spear the centaur-god through the shoulder with Heartrender, screaming a wordless challenge point-blank into Kragnos' face as her mane of serpents bit deep into his neck. The centaur reeled, swiping backhand with his great, lumpen mace, but the goddess's serpentine form swayed aside. Whipping coils wrapped around the Earthquake God's torso to crush the air from his lungs. As the scaly body coiled around his neck, Kragnos sank his teeth deep into the Shadow Queen's flesh, bucking hard to dislodge her grip. Together the two giants toppled into a nearby Sigmarite temple, both thrashing and fighting with desperate intensity to get the upper hand.

In the plaza, Morathi-Khaine took three careful steps backwards before vaulting up onto the low roof of the Coldguard barracks. The advantage of surprise had carried her far, but the brutish god had the strength of Ghur itself behind him. Already he was ripping at her counterpart's coils.

'Kroak of Lustria!' she called to the strange, hovering celestalith and its mummified occupant. The slann was sending bolts of multicoloured light down at Kragnos from his wizened fingers, but the arcane missiles were failing to connect. 'The truth is clear. That which we cannot kill, we must redirect!' At this, the slann's entire stone edifice turned to face her. Hollow sockets gazed into her own, and her mind filled with visions of the star-strewn void, threatening to overwhelm her with their impossible immensity.

'A trap,' she shouted. 'A hole in reality. I shall place the bait!'

The slann held up a bony talon. In the plaza below, a point of unlight pricked the veil of reality, swiftly growing into a roiling circle outlined by crackling blue fire. Morathi-Khaine nodded, pleased by the sight. She could dimly perceive the vista beyond – a vast, spike-walled dreadfort with the snowcapped spine of southern Bjarl's peaks on the horizon. Even the wildernesses of Ghur had not been spared the conquests of Chaos.

'Good enough,' she said. A wave of her hand, and the image in the portal was that of the Draconith Spires in their prime, majestic amber-scaled dragons soaring high above them, just as they had been depicted in the Lenduan Frescoes. Every aspect of her art gave the vision life, but whether it was convincing enough to fool a god had yet to be seen.

She felt an invisible hand at her neck, and the breath went out of her. In the dust of the plaza, her serpent-form coiled and thrashed. Kragnos had proven the stronger in their godly duel and had the Shadow Queen by the throat. His vast mace rose high once more, this time for the kill.

But when it descended, it found only the foundations of Excelsis itself – with a gesture, Morathi-Khaine had turned her counterpart to nothing more than a slithering shadow. As the Dread Mace struck the ground, a network of cracks spread across the entire plaza, much of it collapsing into the under-tunnels below. Kragnos turned towards Morathi-Khaine and her strange, saurian ally. Then came a dragon's cry, and the creature's eyes were drawn to the portal – or, rather, that which shimmered beyond it. His nostrils flared as the sight of his ancient enemies made his blood boil.

The living earthquake looked around himself one last time, drinking in the spectacle of the tumbled, burning city. Already Lord Kroak had turned his celestial magic upon the orruks in the streets, hails of glowing meteors slamming down to crush them into paste. Kragnos ignored the slann altogether, his gaze blazing on Morathi-Khaine as he held out his mace towards her, radiating threat. He said something powerful in the ancient Drogrukh tongue, and, somehow, Morathi understood the intent: 'This is not over.'

Then the End of Empires turned and, with a thunder of hooves, charged straight for the azure ring of Kroak's portal to pass through and disappear in a blaze of light.

grin splitting the daemon's features. Upon appearing in the Realm of Chaos, Synessa and Dexcessa were incensed. Their banishment from Excelsis had been sudden and undignified. Yet as they trailed long claws through fountains of blood, basking in the music of tortured souls and drinking in the sights of the Six Circles for the first time, they came to realise their banishment was not to purgatory but to a paradise – and, better yet, one with an empty throne. Only when a living shadow fell across them did their mood sour.

'And so I find you in the Circle of Indolence,' said Be'lakor. 'How fitting.'

The Dark Master was a presence vast in power and stature, but in Slaanesh's heartland, he seemed as drab and morbid as a carrion crow.

'One might ask who had the more right to be here,' said Synessa.

'One might,' said Dexcessa, taking out their sceptre and setting their stance just so.

'You idle away your time as if in celebration when the God-King's cities still stand?'

victory is a vintage all the sweeter for age.'

'The seed of strife is planted deep,' said Synessa. 'We have made sure of it. It will grow, reaching from Ghur to Hysh to Azyr, until there will never again be a true and lasting accord between man and aelf.'

'And besides, what of your promised endeavours?' asked the Talon. 'The Ghurish sky remained obstinate in its greyness.'

'The shadow lengthens yet,' said Be'lakor. 'It is not only the Crux that is under its pall. And every battle fought under those cursed skies will cost Sigmar dearly, each a cut to his vitals that will slowly bleed him dry.'

'So you too use eternity as a weapon,' said the Voice. 'And you too retreated when a mortal undid your works.'

Be'lakor spread his wings wide amidst a clatter of chain. 'That was no mortal duardin at Vindicarum,' he boomed. 'That was a god, and a powerful one at that. Time is running out.'

There was a flurry of shadow, and Synessa and Dexcessa stood alone once more amongst the screams.

Silence, true and absolute.

It was an acquired taste, but of late, Teclis' heart yearned for it.

The immensity of the aetheric void spread out before him, the glory of Hysh glowing below as his astral form shot past the zenith of the Perimeter Inimical. He could never truly leave that divine light behind, for it was in him, just as he was part of it in turn. But sometimes he wished he could flee into nothingness, or dive down to the darkest depths of the ocean, to finally become numb, quiet and alone.

Just like his first true children, the Cythai, had done long ago to escape their merciless father.

Out here, thought Teclis, he could find a god's perspective. But even here, he was not truly alone.

'That which is put in motion cannot be stopped,' said the moon spirit, its voice a whisper in his mind. 'Will it carry us to the abyss?'

'It may yet,' said Teclis. 'And so the wheel turns.'

'With the blood of countless dead upon it,' said Celennar. 'Would you see it grind the realms to dust?'

'The realms must fight for their own sanctity. Raw chaos infects them. If the natural order itself joins the war, we might still stand a chance.'

'Yet that natural order is corrupted,' said Celennar. 'Do you bring to us as many foes as allies?'

Teclis closed his eyes. Usually he enjoyed these exchanges, the lunar spirit testing his understanding. But this day he felt anger, slowly building.

'All too often, harmony can be found only through war. This I know to be true.'

'You have exchanged one bane for another. Is it wisdom to wake the giant?'

'His chosen are potent but easily outwitted. I judge the sacrifice worthwhile. The war with the greater menace has passed into twilight and is all but over.'

'THE WAR HAS BARELY BEGUN.'

There was a hole there, black and yawning, behind Teclis' vision. His witchsight saw dead stars by the thousand, their horrible absence coalescing to form a hideous, skull-like visage.

'KNOW THIS,' came the voice, echoing across time and space to reach him. 'I WILL END ALL THE THINGS YOU LOVE, ONE BY ONE. THEN, WHEN YOU ARE BROKEN, I WILL TAKE YOUR SOUL.'

'So speaks the vanquished,' said Teclis. 'I have defeated you once; I can do so again.'

'IN BODY, PERHAPS,' came the voice. 'BUT YOU CANNOT OUTRUN DEATH, TECLIS OF ULTHUAN. IN THE END, YOU WILL BE MINE.'

'I have no need to outrun that which I can repel.'

'WITH EVERY PASSING SECOND, YOU COME CLOSER TO YOUR FINAL DEMISE.'

'You have no power over me,' said Teclis, but something in his tone betrayed him.

'YOU KNOW THAT TO BE A LIE. MY VENGEANCE HAS ALREADY BEGUN.'

The dead stars swirled and were gone.

Bogratz sniffed the foul-smelling air of his treetop gantry as startled slop-crows burst from the twisted copses all around. They too knew something big was happening. The murky waters of the mist-wreathed swamp below were rippling, almost as if to a rhythm, and not because of some questing fangsnake or biter-eel on the hunt. The low booms he had been hearing in the back of his mind were now audible.

'Well, Bogratz,' he said to himself. 'Yer a lookout, mate. Better get out there and look.'

Ropy muscles bunching, he climbed even higher up the massive, leafless crawler-oak known as the Shackletree. It had crossed into their swamp a few years back and barely moved since. Plenty of corpses left by its roots, that was the trick. In return, the crawler-oak made an excellent vantage point on the rare occasions when the swamp mists worked against you.

He peered out to the horizon. The booming was coming from the blocky shadow of the spiky humies' castle-city, the one they called Dreadspine Fortress. Bad neighbours to have, but the swamp tribe knew from experience that attacking them head-on was a big mistake. He watched, fascinated, as one then another of their towers toppled. A cloud of dust rose, and on the cusp of hearing, there was a distant roar.

Bogratz unwrapped his seeing stick, the shiny gold long-eye he'd nicked from the corpse of a scout who had strayed too far into the swamp. The humie-thing had essentially got him the nice cushy job of a lookout – although it was a bit cracked and dented, if you looked in the thin end, you could see things in the distance. And what a sight there was today.

There, among the ruins of the castle, was a massive centaur-beast with huge horns and a mane of fiery red hair. It was laying about itself with a giant mace, smashing apart walls even as its hooves trampled the armoured humies trying to stop it. Bogratz had a good hard laugh at the sight, watching the humies frantically running around as their city was smashed to bits. He could have watched it all day long.

'Wot's so zoggin' funny, Bogratz?' The crotchety old voice of the bog-shaman Grokkob rose through the mist to meet him as he emerged from his den under the roots of the tree. 'I'm tryin' ta fink on stuff down 'ere!'

The lookout stowed the long-eye, swung his way down the Shackletree and splashed into the swamp, buzzing with vicious energy. He wanted to stab something, but it'd have to wait. Stabbing a shaman was a surefire way to get turned into a squig. Grokkob squinted up at him, his face a mass of scars and wrinkles. The canny old git could tell something was up.

Bogratz pointed at the scratchy pictograms carved into the crawler-oak's trunk. Among them were pictures of a centaur-god, the ground cracking beneath its hooves.

'It's 'im, boss,' said the sentry, his eyes alight with glee. 'It's da Beast!'

Morathi-Khaine strode into the Excelsium's Conclave Hall with her head held high. The place still stank, the sharp tang of blood mingling with the incense of reconsecration. There he was, at the head of the massive table – the Celestant-Prime, proxy for the God-King himself. Through a gaping wound in the mosaic roof, the city's outer districts could be seen smoking on the horizon. Excelsis had been pulled back from the brink, but it would take decades, if not centuries, to put it right.

Of the two hundred and fifty-six seats at the oval table, only eleven were filled. Still, with her, the essential council was quorate. She checked off the delegates: an ambassador, a strategist, a priest, an engineer, a pioneer, a soldier, a messenger, a pauper, a philosopher, a merchant, a seer, and her, an outsider. It was an old recipe, covering perspectives from the gutter to the highest seat of Azyr. But in Sigmar's eyes, it was deemed enough for the decision to come.

The God-King had not deigned to attend – a strong message in itself – and the slann was already long gone. But the hammer Ghal Maraz lay just in front of the Celestant-Prime, the symbol of Sigmar's judgement. This day, she would face it, for better or for worse.

Morathi-Khaine sat delicately upon the arm of one of the seats. 'So,' she said. 'Let us begin.'

'You are accused of treason against the God-King Sigmar,' intoned the Celestant-Prime. 'This you know.'

'Treason, is it?' she laughed. 'As if I were one of the Heldenhammer's mud-spattered subjects. No, dear mask, I have committed no treason.'

'You engineered a coup of the city Anvilgard in the Great Parch. Did you think it would go unnoticed?'

'For a time,' she said. 'Time enough to prove that my methods, though unorthodox, are for the common good. Have I not proved that beyond all doubt?'

'You fought for Excelsis against Kragnos,' said the Stormcast. 'Even the Fist of Gork retreats to lick his wounds. But it does not excuse the co-opting of a city for your own ends. Do you admit to the theft of Anvilgard?'

'I am a goddess, you gilded fool. I do as I please.'

The Celestant-Prime slowly picked up Ghal Maraz. Above the shattered roof, a score of Knights-Venator winged into view, their enchanted arrows nocked and pointing right at her. Snarling, Morathi-Khaine felt killing power swell in her fingertips.

'And so,' said the Celestant-Prime, 'there can be only one course.'

'Aye,' came a booming voice, filling the hall. 'Aye, lad, and it's clemency.'

A white-bearded duardin thumped into the room, his footsteps carrying the weight of aeons. He was huge and bristling with power.

'The Great Maker,' breathed the Ironweld duardin delegate, scrabbling out of his seat. 'My lord Grungni.' He knelt low as the newcomer took his place.

'None other,' said the duardin god. 'Right, enough bickering, you lot. We've got work to do.'

GODS AND CHAMPIONS

Kragnos unites all subcultures and factions within the hordes of Destruction under his command. All those who revel in the shattering of civilisation see him as both an inspirational figure and a powerful champion.

This section of *Broken Realms: Kragnos* showcases the stunning range of Citadel Miniatures introduced in this book, visible here in all their glory and with details picked out in separate photographs. The models have been expertly painted by the world-famous 'Eavy Metal team.

Kragnos, the End of Empires

Verdigris armour

The Dread Mace

Tuskbreaker, the Shield Inviolate

Reverential totem

Dexcessa, the Talon of Slaanesh

Synessa, the Voice of Slaanesh

Warsong Revenant

Galen ven Denst

Doralia ven Denst

Lord Kroak

THE RULES

BROKEN REALMS

This section of *Broken Realms: Kragnos* contains exciting new rules for open and narrative play games. You can use the rules in this section to recreate the battles that were fought as Kragnos rampaged along the Coast of Tusks.

CAMPAIGN RULES (pg 87)
This section includes a set of rules that allow you to link together the battleplans in this book, so that the result of each battle has an impact on the subsequent battles.

REALMS OF BATTLE (pg 88)
This section includes Realmsphere Magic, Realmscape Features and Realm Artefacts rules that allow you to fight battles set in the location described in the narrative section of the book. These rules have been designed for open and narrative play.

STREETS OF DEATH (pg 89)
This section includes rules that allow you to represent the challenges of fighting battles in the cities of the Mortal Realms.

BATTLEPLANS (pg 90-101)
This section includes new battleplans that allow you to recreate the pivotal battles described in the narrative section of the book. Rather than using measurements, each map shows the battlefield divided into 4 large quarters, each of which is divided into 4 small quarters. This allows you to use the same map for any size of battlefield.

CAMPAIGN RULES

This book includes six battleplans, each based on a critical battle leading up to the Siege of Excelsis. The rules on this page allow you to play a series of linked games that recreates what happened as the fate of the City of Secrets hung in the balance.

THE ARMIES

This campaign is fought between two players. One player is the Order player and the other player is the Destruction player. The Order player must be able to field the following armies from the battleplans on pages 90-101:

- **The Rite of Life:** Sylvaneth Army
- **They Came From Below:** Knights Excelsior Army
- **Clash of Giants:** Kragnos Army*
- **Last Flight of the Scarlet Scourge:** Sky Battalions Army
- **Dark Heart:** Excelsis Army
- **Of Gods and Monsters:** Order Army

The Destruction player must be able to field the following armies:

- **The Rite of Life:** Beastmen Army
- **They Came From Below:** Skaven Army
- **Clash of Giants:** Greenskins Army*
- **Last Flight of the Scarlet Scourge:** Destruction Army
- **Dark Heart:** Slaanesh Army
- **Of Gods and Monsters:** Destruction Army

*Clash of Giants is a 'civil war' with Destruction armies fighting on both sides. If the Order player has models in their collection that allow them to field a Kragnos army, they should use those models. If they do not, the Destruction player should allow the Order player to use their models for this battle.

THE BATTLES

The players must fight each battle in the order in which they appear in this book.

CONSEQUENCES OF BATTLE

Any named characters that are slain in a battle are assumed to have been hurt but not killed, and they will be fully recovered in time for the next battle unless noted otherwise. This aside, the result of an earlier battle may have an impact on subsequent battles that are fought, as explained below. If you are allowed to add units to your army, they must conform to any Unit Selection restrictions for the battleplan being used.

The Rite of Life/They Came From Below/Clash of Giants: No changes.

Last Flight of the Scarlet Scourge: If Gordrakk was slain in Clash of Giants, he does not take part in this battle. Reduce the number of **GYROCOPTERS** and **GYROBOMBERS** units in the Sky Battalions Army from 4 units to 3 if the Order player lost They Came From Below.

Dark Heart: If The White Reaper was slain in They Came From Below, he does not take part in this battle. Add 1 **STORMCAST ETERNALS LIBERATORS** unit of 5 models to the Excelsis Army if the Order player won a **major victory** in They Came From Below, and add another **STORMCAST ETERNALS LIBERATORS** unit of 5 models to the Excelsis Army if the Order player won a **major victory** in Last Flight of the Scarlet Scourge.

Of Gods and Monsters: Add 1 unit to the Destruction Army for each **major victory** the Destruction player has won in the campaign. Reduce the number of units in the Destruction Army by 1 for each **major victory** the Order player has won in the campaign.

CAMPAIGN VICTORY

If one player is victorious in The Rite of Life, Clash of Giants and Of Gods and Monsters, they win a **total campaign victory.** If one player is victorious in The Rite of Life and Of Gods and Monsters, they win a **strategic campaign victory.** In any other circumstances, the victor in Of Gods and Monsters wins a **tactical campaign victory.**

ALTERNATIVE ARMIES

If you don't have all of the units or armies needed to fight a campaign, just substitute suitable units that you do have for the ones that you don't. It's up to you to decide what you think would be appropriate replacements!

REALMS OF BATTLE

On this page, you will find a new set of Realms of Battle rules that allow you to fight battles set in the region of the Mortal Realms described in the narrative section of this book. These rules are suitable for narrative and open play games but are not intended for matched play.

REALM OF BATTLE: THE COAST OF TUSKS, GHUR

REALMSPHERE MAGIC

Wildform: *The wizard transforms their allies into swift-moving bestial forms.*

Wildform has a casting value of 5. If successfully cast, pick 1 friendly unit within 12" of the caster that is visible to them. Add 2 to run and charge rolls for that unit until your next hero phase.

REALMSCAPE FEATURES

The Desolate Wilds: *From the hinterland mists come all manner of greenskin tribes, each hungering for war.*

Add 1" to the Move characteristic and 1 to the Bravery characteristic of all **DESTRUCTION** units. In addition, if you have an Orruk Warclans Big Waaagh! army, you receive an extra D6 Waaagh! points at the start of your first hero phase.

The Clawing Sea: *The Coast of Tusks is bedevilled by oceanic monsters that are drawn to the land in search of easy prey. Even the aelves cannot truly tame these fearsome creatures.*

At the end of each battle round, the players roll off. The winner can set up a Wild Kharibdyss. Use the Kharibdyss warscroll for the Wild Kharibdyss, but do not include the Handlers on the warscroll and do not use the Quick With The Lash ability. Wild Kharibdysses are not part of either army. A Wild Kharibdyss must be set up within 7" of the battlefield edge and more than 9" from all models from either army.

Wild Kharibdysses choose their prey at the start of each battle round. Their prey for that battle round will be the army that has a unit closest to them. For the rest of that battle round, the Wild Kharibdyss joins the opposing army. If both armies have a unit equally close to a Wild Kharibdyss, roll off to determine who chooses the Wild Kharibdyss's prey. Wild Kharibdysses will not choose each other as their prey.

Note that the prey can change each battle round, as Wild Kharibdysses will 'swap sides' depending on which army has a unit closest to them. Also note that a Wild Kharibdyss can attack any unit in their prey's army, not just the closest unit, and it cannot itself be attacked or charged by units from the army it has joined.

REALM ARTEFACT

Glimmering: *Flinders of the Spear of Mallus are traded as 'glimmerings', each yielding visions of events yet to come.*

Once per turn, before you make a hit or wound roll for an attack made by the bearer, a save roll for an attack that targets the bearer, or a run or charge roll for the bearer, you can say that you will foretell the result of the roll. If you do so, you must choose the result of the roll. The result chosen for a D6 roll must be a whole number from 1 to 6, and the result chosen for a 2D6 roll must be a whole number from 2 to 12. The result cannot be re-rolled, but any modifiers are applied to it as normal.

STREETS OF DEATH

The Mortal Realms are studded with settlements, ranging from mighty walled strongholds through to dung-filled wooden shanty towns. In times of war, it is extremely common for ferocious battles to be fought amidst the streets, buildings and alleyways of these hubs of civilisation.

Sometimes a battleplan will use only some of the Streets of Death rules. In this case, it will list the rules that apply. If a battleplan simply says to use the Streets of Death rules, then all of the following rules apply.

The Streets of Death rules are divided into two types: those that can be used with any battleplan and those that can only be used with battleplans that have an attacker and a defender. If a battleplan has an attacker and defender, it will describe how to decide who is the attacker and who is the defender.

The Streets of Death rules often refer to 'buildings'. For rules purposes, a building is any terrain feature that can be garrisoned. In addition, the players can agree that any other terrain features they wish should count as buildings (Azyrite Ruins, for example).

Barricades: *The defenders of a besieged settlement will often place barricades across the streets.*

After set-up is complete but before the battle begins, the defender can set up any number of barricades in their territory. Each barricade must stretch from one building to a different building that is within 8" of the first. The barricade can be represented by Walls and Fences or any other suitable models in the player's collection. Barricades are obstacles.

If a unit is within 1" of a barricade at the start of its movement phase and there are no enemy units within 6" of that barricade, that unit can knock that barricade down instead of making a normal move; if they do so, remove the barricade from the battlefield. A barricade that has been knocked down cannot be set up again.

Bricks and Stones: *The terrified citizens of a settlement can hurl bricks, roof slates and other improvised missiles at their tormentors.*

At the start of their shooting phase, the defender can make 1 Bricks and Stones attack from each building in their territory that has not been cleared (see next). To make a Bricks and Stones attack, pick 1 enemy unit within 6" of that building and roll a dice. On a 5+, that enemy unit suffers D3 mortal wounds.

A building is cleared when an enemy unit garrisons the building. The defender cannot make Bricks and Stones attacks from a building once it has been cleared, even if the enemy unit garrisoning that building stops garrisoning it or if any of the defender's units garrison it.

Hidden Defenders: *Fighting through the streets of a settlement is a tense and dangerous affair, where every building could house hidden defenders.*

Instead of setting them up on the battlefield, the defender can place any of their units to one side and say that they are set up in hiding as reserve units. They must declare that they are doing so for each such unit, and then secretly pick an unoccupied building wholly within their territory and make a note that the unit is hiding in that building. Hidden units are treated as garrisoning that building and must conform to any limitations that apply to garrisoning units.

The defender can reveal the location of any hidden units in their hero phase. In addition, they must reveal a hidden unit if an enemy unit attempts to garrison the building it is hiding in, the building it is hiding in collapses, or the building it is hiding in is set on fire. If a hidden unit is revealed because an enemy unit attempts to garrison the building it is hiding in, the enemy unit cannot garrison the building and cannot move in the movement phase in which it attempted to do so.

Narrow Streets: *The narrow streets of a settlement are dangerous ground for mounted units, who risk crashing into the walls on either side of the street if they advance along them at anything other than a walking pace.*

A narrow street is any area of open ground between two buildings that are 4" or less apart. If a **MONSTER** or a model with a mount makes a run move or charge move, and any part of that move was on a narrow street, roll a dice after the move has been made. On a 1, that model's unit suffers 1 mortal wound after all of the models in the unit have been moved. Only roll for models that can fly if they finish a run move or a charge move on a narrow street.

BATTLEPLAN

THE RITE OF LIFE

The defeat of Nagash in distant Hysh had sent ripples of causality across the realms. In Ghyran, the Everqueen Alarielle was poised to capitalise on this with a grand resurgence, triggering a cascade of consequences both glorious and dire. Opposing her in the stinking, knee-deep swampland were mould-skinned beastmen, their untidy manes matted into slabs that bounced on their shoulders as they ran. Carried by four hulking Ghorgons was the Dirgehorn – that Nurgle-fouled Ghyranite artefact torn from the skull of a godbeast to sound the death of nations, held together with sutures of cankerous flesh to give full voice to its mind-shredding bellow.

THE ARMIES

One player is the Sylvaneth player. Their opponent is the Beastmen player.

Sylvaneth Army

The Sylvaneth player must use a Sylvaneth army. It must consist of the following units and warscroll battalions:

- Alarielle the Everqueen (pg 116)
- Drycha's Spitegrove (pg 119)
- Lords of the Clan (see *Battletome: Sylvaneth*) with 1 Treelord and 2 Treelord Ancients
- 1 Warsong Revenant (pg 117)
- 6 other **SYLVANETH** units

Beastmen Army

The Beastmen player must use a Beasts of Chaos army that has Ghorraghan Khai as its general. It must consist of the following units, warscroll battalion and endless spell:

- The Butcher-herd (pg 133)
- 12 other **BEASTS OF CHAOS** units
- 1 Doomblast Dirgehorn (see *Battletome: Beasts of Chaos*)

Unit Selection

The 'other' units in each army must each conform to one of the types in the following list. You can double the size of a unit if you wish, but it then counts as 2 choices instead of 1.

Regular Unit: A unit of up to 10 models, each with a Wounds characteristic of 1.

Elite Unit: A unit of up to 5 models, each with a Wounds characteristic of 2 or 3.

Guard Unit: A unit of up to 3 models, each with a Wounds characteristic of 4 or 5.

Champion: A **HERO** with a Wounds characteristic of 8 or less.

SET-UP

The Warsong Revenant starts the battle in reserve and will arrive as described opposite.

The Beastmen player must set up The Butcher-herd and the Doomblast Dirgehorn wholly within their territory and wholly within 12" of the middle of the battlefield, with the Doomblast Dirgehorn set up as described opposite.

The players then alternate setting up units one at a time, starting

with the Sylvaneth player. Players must set up units wholly within their territory and more than 9" from enemy territory.

Continue to set up units until both players have set up their armies. If one player finishes first, their opponent must set up the rest of the units in their army, one after another.

THE DIRGEHORN

The Doomblast Dirgehorn endless spell starts the battle already cast and on the battlefield. It must be set up within 3" of the Ghorgon from The Butcher-herd warscroll battalion. It cannot be dispelled except as described below.

The Ghorgon and the Doomblast Dirgehorn are treated as a single model that uses the Ghorgon's warscroll and has the abilities from the Doomblast Dirgehorn's warscroll. The Doomblast Dirgehorn must remain within 1" of the Ghorgon. If the Ghorgon is slain, the Doomblast Dirgehorn is dispelled. In addition, the Doomblast Dirgehorn is dispelled if it ends a move more than 12" from the middle of the battlefield.

THE WARSONG REVENANT

The Warsong Revenant is set up after the Doomblast Dirgehorn is dispelled, within 12" of Alarielle the Everqueen.

BATTLE LENGTH

The battle lasts either for 5 battle rounds or until Alarielle the Everqueen is slain.

GLORIOUS VICTORY

If Alarielle the Everqueen has been slain, the Beastmen player wins a **major victory**. If Alarielle the Everqueen has not been slain, each player adds up the number of enemy units that were destroyed during the battle, excluding any units that were added to the armies after the battle started. Double-sized units count as 2 units instead of 1, and MONSTERS count as 3 units instead of 1.

If the Sylvaneth player has the higher total, they win a **major victory** if the Doomblast Dirgehorn was dispelled and a **minor victory** if it was not dispelled. If the Beastmen player has the higher total, they win a **minor victory** if the Doomblast Dirgehorn was not dispelled, and the battle is a **draw** if it was dispelled.

BATTLEPLAN
THEY CAME FROM BELOW

Excelsis echoed to a thousand screams as the sun set. The assault came not from within, where the strife in the streets had grown to violence, nor from without, where the walls were heavily defended in anticipation of a greenskin attack. Instead, when the eyes of the city's defenders were elsewhere, it came from below. Across the dockyards, mushroom clouds of green smoke blossomed in the wake of ear-ringing explosions, and entire swathes of the street toppled into the sewers to expose the horribly glowing portals below. Gnawholes, the clustered portals were called, splits in the fabric of the realms themselves from which the skaven launched their invasions.

STREETS OF DEATH
Use the Streets of Death rules (pg 89).

THE ARMIES
One player is the Skaven player. Their opponent is the Knights Excelsior player.

Skaven Army
The Skaven player is the attacker and must use a Skaventide army that has Rattachak as its general. It must consist of the following units, warscroll battalion and terrain features:

- Rattachak's Doom-coven (pg 132)
- 9 other **SKAVEN** units
- 3 Gnawhole terrain features (see *Battletome: Skaven*)

Knights Excelsior Army
The Knights Excelsior player is the defender and must use a Stormcast Eternals Knights Excelsior army that has the White Reaper as its general. It must consist of the following units:

- 1 Lord-Veritant (the White Reaper)
- Doralia ven Denst (Cities of Sigmar allied unit, pg 126)
- Galen ven Denst (Cities of Sigmar allied unit, pg 127)
- 10 other **STORMCAST ETERNALS** units

Unit Selection
The 'other' units in each army must each conform to one of the types in the following list. You can double the size of a unit if you wish, but it then counts as 2 choices instead of 1.

Regular Unit: A unit of up to 10 models, each with a Wounds characteristic of 1.

Elite Unit: A unit of up to 5 models, each with a Wounds characteristic of 2 or 3.

Guard Unit: A unit of up to 3 models, each with a Wounds characteristic of 4 or 5.

Champion: A **HERO** with a Wounds characteristic of 8 or less.

THE BATTLEFIELD
Set up the 3 Gnawholes as shown on the map.

This battle is fought on the docks of Excelsis, and appropriate terrain features should be used to represent this.

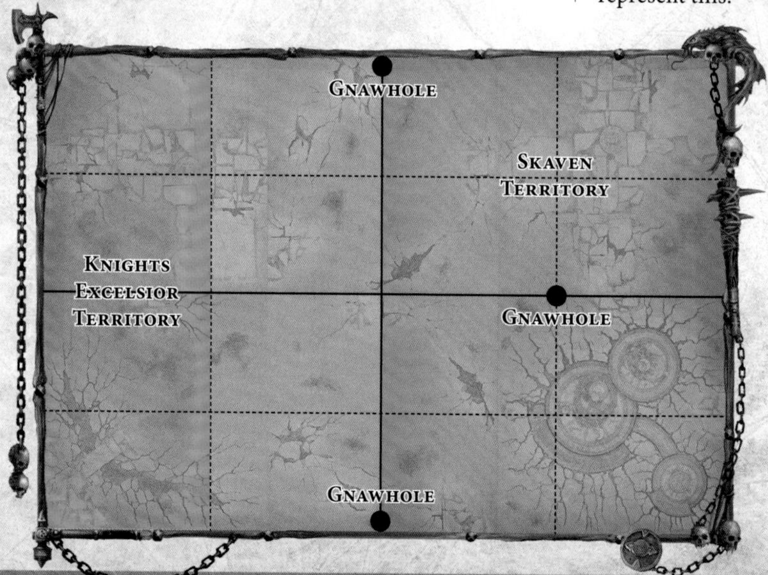

SET-UP

The players alternate setting up units one at a time, starting with the Skaven player. Players must set up units wholly within their territory. Continue to set up units until both players have set up their armies. If one player finishes first, their opponent must set up the rest of the units in their army, one after another.

THE GNAWHOLES

The Knights Excelsior player can treat each Gnawhole as an enemy unit when picking the target of an attack or when picking a unit to suffer mortal wounds. The Gnawhole must be in range of the attack or the ability or spell inflicting mortal wounds. Gnawholes are not treated as units for any other purposes.

Each Gnawhole has a Wounds characteristic of 6 and a Save characteristic of 3+. Once 6 wounds have been allocated to a Gnawhole, it is destroyed and removed from play.

THE WHITE REAPER

The White Reaper is a named character that is a Lord-Veritant. The following special rules apply to the White Reaper:

- You cannot use the Faithful Gryph-hound ability for the White Reaper.
- Roll a dice each time you allocate a wound or mortal wound to the White Reaper. On a 4+, that wound or mortal wound is negated.
- Add 1 to the Attacks characteristic of the White Reaper's Judgement Blade.
- Add 2 to the roll that determines whether the White Reaper's Sanction ability inflicts any mortal wounds.

BATTLE LENGTH

The battle lasts either for 5 battle rounds or until the third Gnawhole is destroyed and removed from play.

GLORIOUS VICTORY

Count the number of Gnawholes that were destroyed during the battle and consult the table below to determine the outcome of the battle.

Destroyed Gnawholes	Outcome
None	Skaven **major victory**
One	Skaven **minor victory**
Two	Knights Excelsior **minor victory**
Three	Knights Excelsior **major victory**

BATTLEPLAN
CLASH OF GIANTS

The End of Empires had finally returned to his homeland – only to find it ground to dust. It had been toppled first by the drake-lords of the north and then by the slow but insatiable ravages of time. There was nothing left of his once-proud nation save a vast chasm, consumed by the continent of Andtor on one side and Thondia on the other. And of his people, there was no sign at all. The only living things Kragnos could see were greenskins amassing a few miles to the south, their leader a hulking, metal-clad brute atop a scaly behemoth almost as big as he was. If they thought to claim the sorry remnants of Donse for their own, they would not live to see another day. With a bellow of anger and sorrow so loud it shook the land entire, Kragnos charged over the lip of the chasm and pounded towards the orruks descending the other side. There was only one thing left for him now: to destroy everything in his path.

REALMS OF BATTLE
This battle uses the rules for the Coast of Tusks, Ghur (pg 88).

THE ARMIES
One player is the Kragnos player. Their opponent is the Greenskins player.

Kragnos Army
The Kragnos player must use a Sons of Behemat army. It must consist of the following units:

- Kragnos, the End of Empires (pg 106)
- 1 Kraken-eater Mega-Gargant (Derko Walrusbiter)
- 1 Warstomper Mega-Gargant
- 3 Mancrusher Gargants units, each with 1 model

Greenskins Army
The Greenskins player must use an Orruk Warclans Big Waaagh! army that has Gordrakk as its general. It must consist of the following units:

- Gordrakk, the Fist of Gork
- Skragrott, the Loonking (Gloomspite Gitz allied unit)
- 10 other **ORRUK WARCLANS** units
- 2 other **GLOOMSPITE GITZ** allied units

Unit Selection
The 'other' units in each army must each conform to one of the types in the following list. You can double the size of a unit if you wish, but it then counts as 2 choices instead of 1.

Regular Unit: A unit of up to 10 models, each with a Wounds characteristic of 1.

Elite Unit: A unit of up to 5 models, each with a Wounds characteristic of 2 or 3.

Guard Unit: A unit of up to 3 models, each with a Wounds characteristic of 4 or 5.

Champion: A **HERO** with a Wounds characteristic of 8 or less.

SET-UP

The players alternate setting up units one at a time, starting with the Greenskins player. Players must set up units wholly within their territory.

Continue to set up units until both players have set up their armies. If one player finishes first, their opponent must set up the rest of the units in their army, one after another.

THE BAD MOON

The Greenskins player can use the Bad Moon and Light of the Bad Moon battle traits from *Battletome: Gloomspite Gitz* even though they are not using a Gloomspite Gitz army. In addition, the Greenskins player can use the following Light of the Bad Moon ability in addition to any other Light of the Bad Moon abilities they can use:

Bad Moon Barrier: Once per battle, if **SKRAGROTT** is on the battlefield at the start of the combat phase, you can roll a dice. On a 2+, you can pick 1 friendly unit that is visible to **SKRAGROTT** and affected by the light of the Bad Moon. That unit cannot attack or be attacked in that combat phase.

BATTLE LENGTH

The battle lasts either for 5 battle rounds or until a player wins a **major victory**.

GLORIOUS VICTORY

If Kragnos was slain by an attack made with a melee weapon by Gordrakk, the Greenskins player wins a **major victory**. If Gordrakk was slain by an attack made with a melee weapon by Kragnos, the Kragnos player wins a **major victory**.

If neither player has won a **major victory**, each player adds up the number of enemy units that were destroyed during the battle, excluding any units that were added to the armies after the battle started. Double-sized units count as 2 units instead of 1; Kragnos, Gordrakk and Derko Walrusbiter count as 5 units instead of 1; and any other **MONSTERS** count as 2 units instead of 1. The player with the higher total wins a **minor victory**. If both players have the same total, the battle is a **draw**.

BATTLEPLAN

LAST FLIGHT OF THE SCARLET SCOURGE

The Gyrocopters and bombers of the sky battalions of Excelsis took flight en masse, their advance covered by low-hanging clouds conjured by the Collegiate wizards' tower-mounted Hurricanums. Led by a cherry-red craft with an impressive array of guns known as the Scarlet Scourge, the sky battalions prepared to attack...

REALMS OF BATTLE

This battle uses the rules for the Coast of Tusks, Ghur (pg 88).

THE ARMIES

One player is the Sky Battalions player. Their opponent is the Destruction player.

Sky Battalions Army

The Sky Battalions player must use a Cities of Sigmar Excelsis army that has the Scarlet Scourge as its general. It must consist of the following units:

- 1 Gyrobombers unit of 1 model (The Scarlet Scourge)
- 4 Gyrocopters or Gyrobombers units in any combination, each with up to 3 models

Destruction Army

The Destruction player must use the following army that has Gordrakk as its general. This army includes **ORRUK WARCLANS** units, **GLOOMSPITE GITZ** units and **SONS OF BEHEMAT** units. It does not belong to a specific faction and does not have any allegiance abilities, and it must consist of the following units:

- Gordrakk, the Fist of Gork
- 1 Dankhold Troggoths unit of 1 model
- 2 Fellwater Troggoths or Rockgut Troggoths units in any combination, each with 3 models
- 1 **MEGA-GARGANT**
- 1 Mancrusher Gargants unit of up to 3 models

SET-UP

The Destruction player sets up their army first, wholly within their territory. The Sky Battalions player sets up their army second, wholly within their territory.

FIRST TURN

The Sky Battalions player takes the first turn in the first battle round.

THE SCARLET SCOURGE

The Scarlet Scourge's Clattergun has an Attacks characteristic of 8 instead of 4. In addition, when the Sky Battalions player uses the Scarlet Scourge's Grudgebuster Bombs ability, they can roll 2 dice when the model passes across any models in the enemy unit instead of 1.

UP, UP AND AWAY

After the Sky Battalions player makes a normal move with a friendly unit, they can say that the unit is flying up, up and away.

If they do so, until their next movement phase, that unit cannot charge, and when measuring the distance between that unit and another unit in the shooting phase and the combat phase to determine whether either is in range of an attack, add 6".

YOU CAN'T GET AWAY FROM ME!

At the start of the combat phase, the Destruction player can pick 1 friendly model that is within 3" of any enemy units that are flying up, up and away and roll a dice. Add 2 to the roll if the friendly model is a MONSTER. On a 4+, until the end of that phase, when measuring the distance between that model and an enemy unit that is flying up, up and away to determine whether it is in range of an attack, do not add 6".

BATTLE LENGTH

The battle lasts either for 5 battle rounds or until Gordrakk is slain.

GLORIOUS VICTORY

If Gordrakk has been slain, the Sky Battalions player wins a **major victory**. In all other circumstances, each player adds up the number of enemy units that were destroyed during the battle. Double-sized units count as 2 units instead of 1; MEGA-GARGANTS count as 5 units instead of 1; and any other MONSTERS count as 2 units instead of 1.

If the Destruction player has the higher total and the Scarlet Scourge has been slain, they win a **major victory**. Otherwise, the player with the higher total wins a **minor victory**. If both players have the same total, the battle is a **draw**.

BATTLEPLAN
DARK HEART

Galen and Doralia ven Denst fought their way towards the canker at Excelsis's heart. With them came the White Reaper, for he too had seen the dire cavalcade of Slaaneshi daemons from afar and felt a great disquiet that only tackling them in person would diminish. The trio entered the Conclave Hall to see that battle still raged in the palace. Galen and Doralia levelled their weapons, sending nullstone bullet and rune-inscribed stake hurtling across the room to strike the daemon giants in their backs, liberating the Grand Matriarch Yarga-Sjuhan and her honour guard from the spells that enthralled them. Almost immediately, violent combat erupted in the gore-drenched hall.

THE ARMIES

One player is the Slaanesh player. Their opponent is the Excelsis player.

Slaanesh Army

The Slaanesh player must use a Hedonites of Slaanesh army. It must consist of the following units and warscroll battalion:

- Dexcessa, the Talon of Slaanesh (pg 120)
- Synessa, the Voice of Slaanesh (pg 122)
- The Exquisite Pursuit (pg 123)
- 2 Daemonettes units, each with 10 models

Excelsis Army

The Excelsis player must use a Cities of Sigmar Excelsis army that has Yarga-Sjuhan as its general. It must consist of the following units:

- 1 Battlemage (Yarga-Sjuhan)
- 1 Freeguild Greatswords unit of 10 models (the Honour Guard)
- 1 Lord-Veritant (the White Reaper, Stormcast Eternals allied unit)
- Doralia ven Denst (pg 126)
- Galen ven Denst (pg 127)

THE BATTLEFIELD

This battle is fought at close-quarters in the Conclave Hall. Units cannot make any part of a move into or through the areas marked black on the map.

SET-UP

The Excelsis player must set up Yarga-Sjuhan and the Honour Guard first. Yarga-Sjuhan must be set up in the centre of the Grand Matriarch's territory, and then the Honour Guard must be set up wholly within 6" of her.

The Slaanesh player then sets up their army wholly within their territory and more than 3" from any enemy units.

Finally, the Excelsis player sets up their remaining models wholly within the Rescuers' territory and more than 3" from any enemy units.

FIRST TURN

The Excelsis player takes the first turn in the first battle round.

THE WHITE REAPER

The White Reaper is a named character that is a Lord-Veritant. The following special rules apply to the White Reaper:

- You cannot use the Faithful Gryph-hound ability for the White Reaper.
- Roll a dice each time you allocate a wound or mortal wound to the White Reaper. On a 4+, that wound or mortal wound is negated.
- Add 1 to the Attacks characteristic of the White Reaper's Judgement Blade.
- Add 2 to the roll that determines whether the White Reaper's Sanction ability inflicts any mortal wounds.

GRAND MATRIARCH

The Honour Guard is Yarga-Sjuhan's retinue for the purposes of the Honoured Retinue battle trait, and Yarga-Sjuhan gains the Loyal Shields ability (see *Battletome: Cities of Sigmar*).

AMBERBONE NECKLACES

Add 1 to the Attacks characteristic of weapons used by the Honour Guard in the first battle round, and add 2 to run and charge rolls for the Honour Guard in the first battle round.

SANCTUM

Neither player can add extra models to their army or return slain models to a unit during this battle.

BATTLE LENGTH

The battle lasts until all of the models in one of the armies have been slain.

GLORIOUS VICTORY

The player with any models remaining on the battlefield at the end of the battle is the winner. If the winner has at least 2 HEROES on the battlefield at the end of the battle, they win a **major victory**. Otherwise, they win a **minor victory**. In the unlikely event that neither side has any models remaining on the battlefield, the battle is a **draw**.

BATTLEPLAN
OF GODS AND MONSTERS

As a long day of battle raged on into night, it was becoming clear that the intervention of the Stormcast Eternals would not be enough. At the breaches, at the harbour, even from the tunnels below the city, greenskins were breaking through to run pell-mell through the streets. Excelsis's lifespan could be measured in hours at most. Then, from the mists of the harbour, a hundred tall sails emerged into view. Morathi-Khaine had come, and from the darkest quarter, Excelsis had been given hope anew.

STREETS OF DEATH
Use the Streets of Death rules (pg 89).

THE ARMIES
One player is the Order player. Their opponent is the Destruction player.

Order Army
The Order player must use the following army. This army includes **CITIES OF SIGMAR** units, **DAUGHTERS OF KHAINE** units, **SERAPHON** units and **STORMCAST ETERNALS** units. It does not belong to a specific faction and does not have any allegiance abilities, and it must consist of the following units:

- Lord Kroak (pg 128)
- Morathi-Khaine (see *Broken Realms: Morathi*)
- The Shadow Queen (see *Broken Realms: Morathi*)
- 12 **SCOURGE PRIVATEERS** units
- 2 **MELUSAI** units
- 12 **STORMCAST ETERNALS** units

Destruction Army
The Destruction player must use the following army. This army includes **ORRUK WARCLANS** units, **GLOOMSPITE GITZ** units and **SONS OF BEHEMAT** units. It does not belong to a specific faction and does not have any allegiance abilities, and it must consist of the following units:

- Kragnos, the End of Empires (pg 106)
- 1 **MEGA-GARGANT**
- 1 Mancrusher Gargants unit of up to 3 models
- 12 **ORRUK WARCLANS** units
- 8 **GLOOMSPITE GITZ** units

Unit Selection
The **SCOURGE PRIVATEERS**, **STORMCAST ETERNALS**, **ORRUK WARCLANS** and **GLOOMSPITE GITZ** units in each army must each conform to one of the types in the following list. You can double the size of a unit if you wish, but it then counts as 2 choices instead of 1.

Regular Unit: A unit of up to 10 models, each with a Wounds characteristic of 1.

Elite Unit: A unit of up to 5 models, each with a Wounds characteristic of 2 or 3.

Guard Unit: A unit of up to 3 models, each with a Wounds characteristic of 4 or 5.

Champion: A **HERO** with a Wounds characteristic of 8 or less.

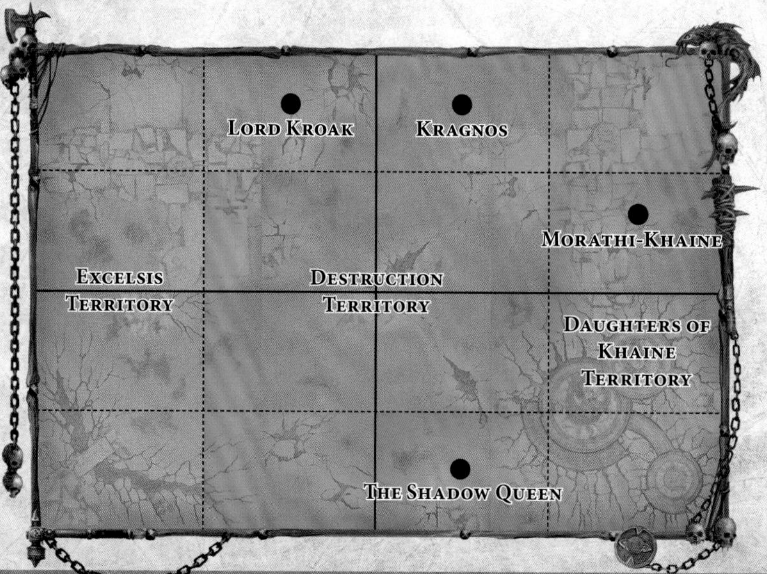

THE BATTLEFIELD

This battle is fought on the streets of Excelsis, and appropriate terrain features should be used to represent this.

SET-UP

The battlefield is divided into 16 areas as shown on the map. Lord Kroak, Kragnos, Morathi-Khaine and the Shadow Queen are set up first in the centre of the areas marked for them on the map.

The players alternate setting up their remaining units one at a time, starting with the Destruction player. **STORMCAST ETERNALS** units must be set up wholly within Excelsis territory, **SCOURGE PRIVATEERS** and **DAUGHTERS OF KHAINE** units wholly within Daughters of Khaine territory, and **DESTRUCTION** units wholly within Destruction territory. All units must be set up more than 6" from any enemy units.

Continue to set up units until both players have set up their armies. If one player finishes first, their opponent must set up the rest of the units in their army, one after another.

BANISHMENT

At the end of each battle round, the Order player can attempt to banish Kragnos. In order to do so, all of the following criteria must be met:

- Morathi-Khaine and Lord Kroak are within 3" of each other, and neither model is within 3" of any enemy units.
- Kragnos is within 3" of an enemy unit.

To attempt to banish Kragnos, the Order player must roll a dice. On a 2+, Kragnos is removed from play but does not count as having been slain.

BATTLE LENGTH

The battle either lasts for 5 battle rounds or until Kragnos is slain.

GLORIOUS VICTORY

If Kragnos has been slain, the Order player wins a **major victory**. In any other circumstances, each player adds up the number of enemy units that were destroyed during the battle. Double-sized units count as 2 units instead of 1; Lord Kroak, Morathi-Khaine, the Shadow Queen and **MEGA-GARGANTS** count as 5 models instead of 1, and any other **MONSTERS** count as 2 units instead of 1.

If the Destruction player has the higher total and Kragnos was not banished, they win a **major victory**. Otherwise, the player with the higher total wins a **minor victory**. If both players have the same total, the battle is a **draw**.

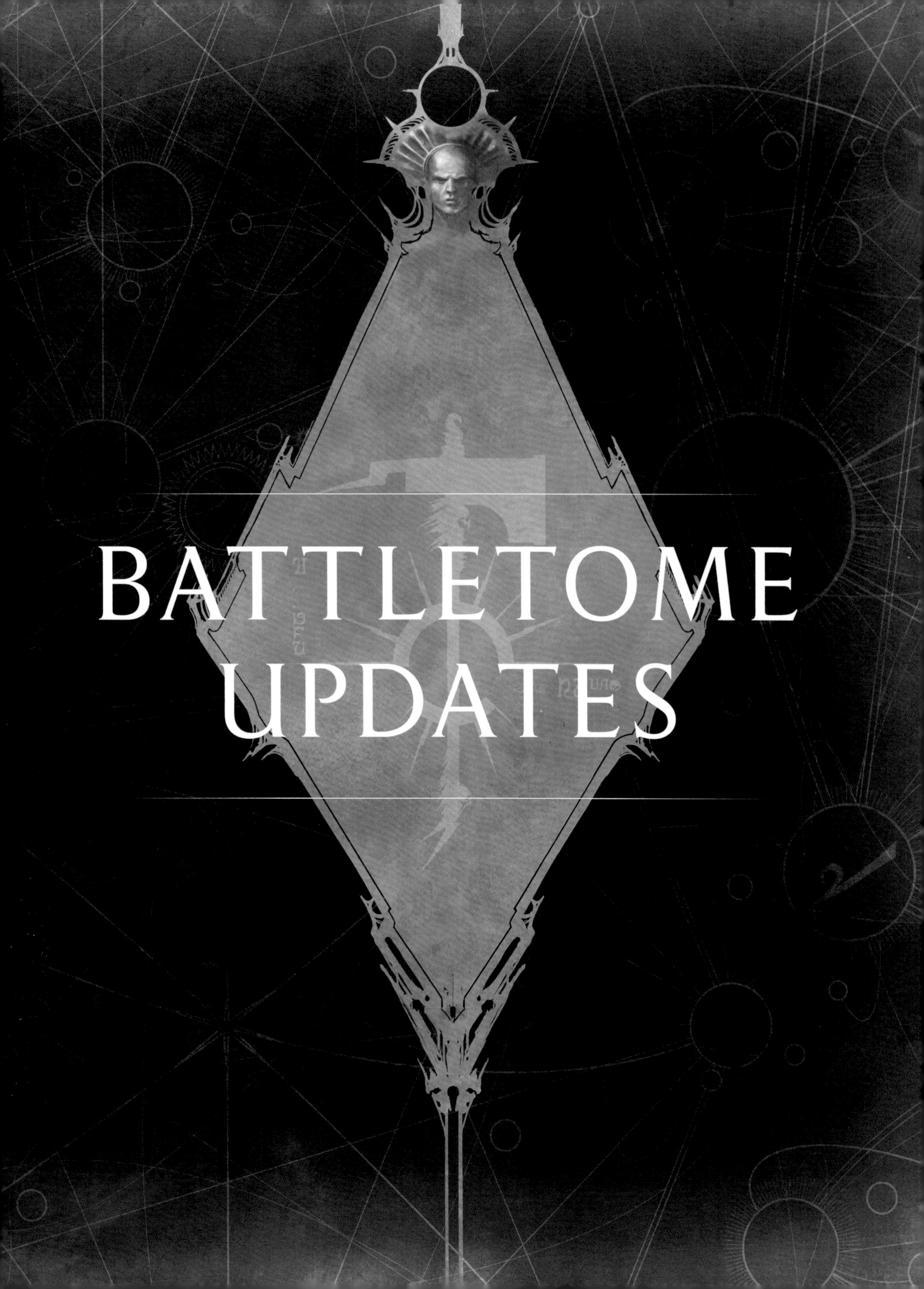

BATTLETOME UPDATES

BATTLETOME UPDATES

This section of *Broken Realms: Kragnos* contains rules for using Kragnos in your games of Warhammer Age of Sigmar and updates for seven battletomes, including new allegiance abilities, battalions and warscrolls. These rules are designed to be used with the battleplans in this book and can also be used in matched play.

KRAGNOS, THE END OF EMPIRES (pg 106)
Here you will find a warscroll for the formidable Kragnos, the End of Empires, and rules that explain which armies he can ally with.

GLOOMSPITE GITZ (pg 108-115)
Battletome: Gloomspite Gitz receives updates to the Bad Moon Loonshrine scenery warscroll together with new allegiance abilities and warscroll battalions that allow you to field Jaws of Mork, Glogg's Megamob and Grimscuttle armies.

SYLVANETH (pg 116-119)
This update to *Battletome: Sylvaneth* contains the Drycha's Spitegrove warscroll battalion, new warscrolls for Alarielle the Everqueen and the Warsong Revenant, and updates to the Awakened Wyldwood scenery warscroll.

HEDONITES OF SLAANESH (pg 120-123)
The *Battletome: Hedonites of Slaanesh* update consists of new warscrolls for Dexcessa, the Talon of Slaanesh, and Synessa, the Voice of Slaanesh, as well as the warscroll battalion for the Exquisite Pursuit.

CITIES OF SIGMAR (pg 124-127)
Rules for fielding a Cities of Sigmar army from Excelsis and new warscrolls for Doralia and Galen ven Denst can be found in this update to *Battletome: Cities of Sigmar.*

SERAPHON (pg 128)
Battletome: Seraphon receives a new warscroll for the mightiest of the slann, Lord Kroak.

SKAVEN (pg 130-132)
This update to *Battletome: Skaven* contains rules that allow you to hide Clans Skryre weapon teams in other Skaventide units, Clans Moulder mutations for Rat Ogors and Hell Pit Abominations, and the Rattachak's Doom-coven warscroll battalion.

BEASTS OF CHAOS (pg 133-135)
The *Battletome: Beasts of Chaos* update includes new Primal Instincts battle traits, updated warscrolls for the Beastlord and Jabberslythe, and the warscroll battalion for the Butcher-herd.

PITCHED BATTLE PROFILES (pg 136)
Here you will find Pitched Battle profiles for all of the warscrolls and warscroll battalions in this book.

• WARSCROLL •

KRAGNOS

THE END OF EMPIRES

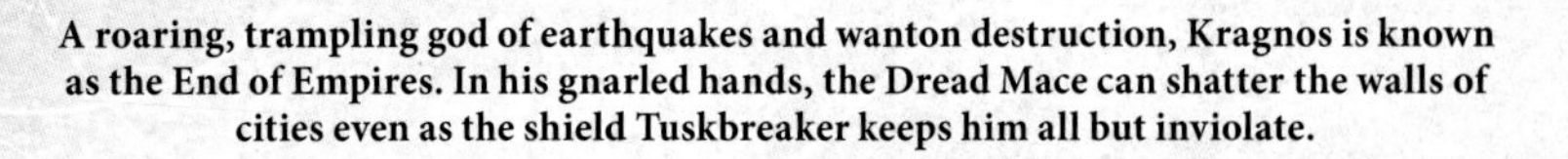
A roaring, trampling god of earthquakes and wanton destruction, Kragnos is known as the End of Empires. In his gnarled hands, the Dread Mace can shatter the walls of cities even as the shield Tuskbreaker keeps him all but inviolate.

MELEE WEAPONS	Range	Attacks	To Hit	To Wound	Rend	Damage
The Dread Mace	3"	6	3+	2+	-3	4
Tuskbreaker	1"	3	3+	2+	-2	D3
Hooves of Wrack and Ruin	1"	✹	3+	2+	-1	2

DAMAGE TABLE			
Wounds Suffered	Move	Hooves of Wrack and Ruin	Bellow of Rage
0-9	10"	6	5+
10-12	9"	5	4+
13-15	8"	4	3+
16+	7"	3	2+

DESCRIPTION

Kragnos, the End of Empires, is a named character that is a single model. He is armed with the Dread Mace, Tuskbreaker and Hooves of Wrack and Ruin.

If Kragnos is included in an army whose general has the DESTRUCTION keyword, Kragnos is treated as a general in addition to the model that is chosen to be the army general.

ABILITIES

Bellow of Rage: *When wounded, Kragnos bellows at the top of his lungs, the sound waves bursting the eardrums of those nearby and rocking buildings at their foundations.*

At the end of any phase, if any wounds were allocated to this model in that phase and not negated, roll a dice for each other unit and each defensible terrain feature within 6" of this model. If the roll is equal to or greater than the Bellow of Rage value shown on this model's damage table, that unit suffers D3 mortal wounds or that defensible terrain feature is demolished.

Designer's Note: *Any terrain feature that can be garrisoned is considered to be a defensible terrain feature for the purposes of this rule. If a defensible terrain feature is demolished, it is no longer considered to be a defensible terrain feature, all units garrisoning it must leave and it can no longer be garrisoned, but models can move onto and across it.*

If a defensible terrain feature is being garrisoned when it is demolished, roll a dice for each model in the garrison. On a 1, that model is slain. The surviving models from the garrison must then be set up within 6" of the terrain feature and more than 3" from all enemy units.

Destroyer of the Draconith Empire: *Kragnos hunted down dragonkind across all of the ancient realms and carries an abiding hatred of their kin to this day.*

You can re-roll charge rolls and hit rolls for this model while it is within 12" of any enemy STARDRAKES, DRAKES, DRACOTHS or DRACOLINES.

Rampaging Destruction: *This galloping god pounds through the press of his foes, his hooves flattening armoured warriors left and right.*

After this model makes a charge move, you can either roll a dice for each enemy unit that is within 1" of this model or you can pick 1 enemy MONSTER within 1" of this model and roll 2D6.

If you roll a dice for each enemy unit within 1" of this model, on a 2+, that unit suffers D6 mortal wounds.

If you pick 1 enemy MONSTER within 1" of this model and roll 2D6, on a 7, nothing happens. On any other roll, that MONSTER suffers a number of mortal wounds equal to the score of the dice used for the 2D6 roll multiplied together. For example, a 2D6 roll of 2 and 6 would inflict 12 mortal wounds (2 × 6 = 12).

Icon of Destruction: *Kragnos is revered and held in awe by all warriors that belong to the Grand Alliance of Destruction.*

Add 1 to the Bravery characteristic of friendly DESTRUCTION units wholly within 12" of this model.

The Shield Inviolate: *Tuskbreaker makes Kragnos impervious to even the most potent magical hexes and bolts.*

Each time this model is affected by a spell or an endless spell ability, you can roll 3D6. If the roll is greater than the casting value of that spell or endless spell, ignore the effects of that spell or that endless spell ability on this model.

Designer's Note: *Use the casting value on the spell or endless spell's warscroll, not the casting roll for the spell or endless spell.*

You can include Kragnos in a DESTRUCTION army even if he does not have the army's keyword on his warscroll. If you do so, he cannot use or benefit from any of that army's allegiance abilities, and you cannot include any mercenary units in your army.

KEYWORDS	DESTRUCTION, MONSTER, HERO, KRAGNOS

BAD MOON LOONSHRINE

The Bad Moon is said to be made entirely of a strange substance known as loonstone. As it sails through the skies of the realms, the Bad Moon sporadically spits out meteoric shards of loonstone that plummet to the ground, which the greenskins painstakingly carve into Loonshrines in the Bad Moon's honour.

A Gloomspite Gitz army can include 1 Bad Moon Loonshrine terrain feature (see opposite).

'It begins with strange storms that tear at the sky and fill it with cloud-tatters like a grotling's ragged cloak. Up becomes down as weird forces go to work, and the honest magics of the realms are set askew. Rivers run backwards, beasts turn endless widdershin circles till exhaustion takes them, and swarms of slime-slick insects come crawling from every cranny and hole.

Then comes the Bad Moon, looming through the broken clouds. As its leering face fills the sky, the heavens vanish from sight till all is lit instead with twilight's sickly glow. The fungus bursts forth, then, and the ground shakes and shudders like a sickening beast or a carcass with maggots crawling thick beneath its rippling hide.

Out come the grotlings, sure as Elder Bones waits beyond the doors of death, and as they spill forth, down come the Bad Moon's fangs. It spits 'em out by the mouthful and they plummet like rocky rain upon them doomed lands below.

Smashing and crashing they fall, to the ruin of all beneath them, and so high do the spores billow up from the craters they blast that the folk take to callin' them mushroom clouds. Yet it doesn't end there.

The grotlings come scurrying. The grotlings set to carving. Before long, what fell as a mound of shapeless, glowing rock becomes a ghastly face. Loonshrines, they call them, but I'd say their name is death itself. Tunnels there are beneath these horrible graven effigies, and from out of them the grotlings spew like vomit from a fluxrot victim's mouth. Foul fungi pepper the shrines from bottom to top, and they quiver and shudder in the rancid winds, spilling clouds of spores that catch in the eyes and throat, that dig into the flesh and cause terrible changes to take hold.

The worst, though, is the eyes. Hewn from stone as they are, I tell you sure as I stand here, those eyes can see. The longer you stare, the more they stare back, and as the loonlight shines within 'em and the shuddering circles roll and twist in their depths, oh, then you feel your mind begin to leak away into the dark and dank where it'll wander lost for evermore. Hear me in this if nothing else – don't go near the Loonshrines!'

- From the ravings of Vincente Falandri, inmate of the Grand Asylum of Hammerhal Ghyra

• SCENERY WARSCROLL •

BAD MOON LOONSHRINE

Where the Fangz of the Bad Moon fall, they smash down upon the landscape causing untold devastation. Then come the Gloomspite hordes, creeping from below to hew these loonstone outcroppings into grotesque shrinelairs that soon become encrusted with fungi and imbued with the sinister energies of their progenitor rock.

DESCRIPTION

A Bad Moon Loonshrine is a single terrain feature. It is an obstacle.

If your army includes a Bad Moon Loonshrine, after territories have been determined but before armies are set up, you must set up the Bad Moon Loonshrine wholly within your territory, more than 12" from enemy territory and more than 1" from all other terrain features and objectives. If both players can set up terrain features before armies are set up, the players must roll off, and the winner chooses who sets up their terrain features first.

SCENERY RULES

Loonatic Courage: *Large loonstone meteorites are hacked into crude effigies of the Bad Moon, inspiring fanatical courage in its servants.*

GLOOMSPITE GITZ units wholly within 12" of this terrain feature do not take battleshock tests.

Moonclan Lairs: *The Gloomspite Gitz use Moonclan-dug tunnels to reach nearby Loonshrines. In battle, reinforcements emerge from these echoing subterranean passages.*

At the end of each of your turns, you can pick 1 friendly STABBAS or SHOOTAS unit that has been destroyed. If your general has the SPIDERFANG keyword, you must pick 1 friendly SPIDER RIDERS unit that has been destroyed instead. If your general has the SQUIG keyword, you must pick 1 friendly SQUIG HERD, SQUIG HOPPERS or BOINGROT BOUNDERZ unit that has been destroyed instead. If your general has the TROGGOTH keyword, you must pick 1 friendly TROGGOTH unit with a Wounds characteristic of 5 or less that has been destroyed instead.

After you pick a unit that has been destroyed, roll a dice. On a 4+, a new replacement unit with half of the models from the unit that was destroyed (rounding up) is added to your army. Set up that unit wholly within 12" of a friendly BAD MOON LOONSHRINE and more than 3" from any enemy units. Each destroyed unit can only be replaced once – replacement units cannot themselves be replaced.

KEYWORDS	SCENERY, GLOOMSPITE GITZ, BAD MOON LOONSHRINE

JAWS OF MORK ALLEGIANCE ABILITIES

If your army is a Gloomspite Gitz army, you can give it the JAWS OF MORK keyword. All Gloomspite Gitz units in your army gain that keyword, and you can use the following allegiance abilities in addition to the allegiance abilities in *Battletome: Gloomspite Gitz*.

THE JAWS BITE DOWN

JAWS OF MORK armies only.

ABILITIES

Running Riot: *The Jaws of Mork are all too eager to unleash themselves upon the enemy, for the sooner they begin their rampage, the sooner they can catch up to the Bad Moon and leap right over it.*

You can re-roll the roll that determines the Move characteristic of friendly **JAWS OF MORK SQUIG** units.

COMMAND ABILITY

'Get Some Loonshine Down 'Em!': *The strange fungal growths that sprout across the Yskian Veldt are used by the Jaws of Mork to work their mightiest war beasts into a terrible, heedless frenzy.*

You can use this command ability at the start of any phase. If you do so, pick 1 friendly **JAWS OF MORK MANGLER SQUIGS** model. Until the end of that phase, use the top row on that model's damage table, regardless of how many wounds it has suffered.

COMMAND TRAIT

A **JAWS OF MORK** general must have this command trait instead of one listed on pages 62-63 of *Battletome: Gloomspite Gitz.*

Envoy of the Overbounder: *The presence of the Overbounder, or one of his favoured bosses, sees the manic and disorganised Jaws of Mork fight with something almost approaching focused courage. Almost.*

You can re-roll failed battleshock tests for friendly **JAWS OF MORK** units wholly within 12" of this general.

ARTEFACT OF POWER

The first **JAWS OF MORK HERO** to receive an artefact of power must be given a Syari Screamersquig.

Syari Screamersquig: *This rare breed of squig screams incessantly when exposed to light, startling even the most resolute warriors and leaving them vulnerable to a sneaky shivving.*

At the start of the combat phase, you can pick 1 enemy **HERO** within 3" of the bearer. If you do so, until your next hero phase, add 1 to hit rolls for attacks made with melee weapons by the bearer that target that **HERO**.

JAWS OF MORK WARSCROLL BATTALION
MOON-JUMPER STAMPEDE

ORGANISATION

A Moon-Jumper Stampede consists of the following units:

- 2-3 **Jaws of Mork** Squig Hoppers units or **Jaws of Mork** Boingrot Bounderz units in any combination
- 0-1 **Jaws of Mork** Mangler Squigs

ABILITIES

Crushing Gobs: *The fertile soil of Yska produces not only bounder squigs of immense size but also beasts with overwhelming power in their fang-lined jaws.*

Add 1 to the Damage characteristic of Fang-filled Gobs and Huge Fang-filled Gobs used by units from this battalion if they made a charge move in the same turn.

JAWS OF MORK WARSCROLL BATTALION
MOON-BITER SQUIGALANCHE

ORGANISATION

A Moon-Biter Squigalanche consists of the following units:

- 1 **Jaws of Mork** Loonboss on Mangler Squigs or 1 **Jaws of Mork** Loonboss on Giant Cave Squig
- 0-3 **Jaws of Mork** Loonbosses on Giant Cave Squig
- 1+ **Jaws of Mork** Moon-Jumper Stampedes
- 1-3 **Jaws of Mork** Mangler Squigs
- 0-2 **Jaws of Mork** Squig Herd units

ABILITIES

Overbounding Loonatics: *The beady-eyed hooligans of a Moon-Biter Squigalanche lunge at the enemy as if they were the Bad Moon itself.*

After armies have been set up but before the first battle round begins, up to D3 units from this battalion can move up to 6". If both players can move units after armies have been set up, the players must roll off, and the winner chooses who moves their units first.

GLOGG'S MEGAMOB ALLEGIANCE ABILITIES

If your army is a Gloomspite Gitz army, you can give it the GLOGG'S MEGAMOB keyword. All Gloomspite Gitz units in your army gain that keyword, and you can use the following allegiance abilities in addition to the allegiance abilities in *Battletome: Gloomspite Gitz*.

THE TROGGOTHS LUMBER ONWARDS

GLOGG'S MEGAMOB armies only.

ABILITIES

Monstrous Regeneration: *The arcane fungal diet of Glogg's Megamob has boosted the regenerative powers of the troggoths to new heights.*

Add 1 to the dice that determines if a friendly **GLOGG'S MEGAMOB TROGGOTH** unit heals any wounds when it uses its Regeneration ability.

COMMAND ABILITY

Oblivious to Sorcery: *A meaningful grunt from one of Glogg's Troggbosses can compel its followers to shrug off even the most potent magical assaults.*

You can use this command ability in your hero phase. If you do so, pick 1 friendly **GLOGG'S MEGAMOB FELLWATER TROGGOTH** or **GLOGG'S MEGAMOB ROCKGUT TROGGOTH** unit wholly within 12" of a friendly **GLOGG'S MEGAMOB DANKHOLD HERO**. Until your next hero phase, each time that unit is affected by a spell or endless spell, you can roll a dice. If you do so, on a 4+, ignore the effects of that spell or endless spell on that unit.

COMMAND TRAIT

A **GLOGG'S MEGAMOB** general must have the following command trait:

Shepherd of Idiotic Destruction: *The many Dankholds of Glogg's Megamob are capable of acting with something almost approaching cohesion when led by one of their brutish bosses.*

If this general is part of your army and on the battlefield at the start of your hero phase, roll a dice. On a 4+, you receive 1 extra command point.

ARTEFACT OF POWER

The first **GLOGG'S MEGAMOB TROGGOTH HERO** to receive an artefact of power must be given the Aetherquartz-studded Hide.

Aetherquartz-studded Hide: *On their travels, this troggoth has picked up many prisms of aetherquartz and stuck them into its tough flesh. Though it almost certainly has no idea why it did so, the power of the Hyshian realmstone nevertheless lends it surprising resilience.*

Roll a dice each time you allocate a mortal wound to the bearer. On a 5+, that mortal wound is negated.

GLOGG'S MEGAMOB WARSCROLL BATTALION
STOMPING MEGAMOB

ORGANISATION

A Stomping Megamob consists of the following units:

- 1 **Glogg's Megamob** Dankhold Troggboss
- 3-9 **Glogg's Megamob** Dankhold Troggoths, **Glogg's Megamob** Fellwater Troggoths or **Glogg's Megamob** Rockgut Troggoths units in any combination
- 0-2 **Glogg's Megamob** Aleguzzler Gargants

ABILITIES

One-track Minds: *When the troggoths of this belligerent horde get going, they can prove incredibly difficult to stop.*

Units from this battalion can retreat and still shoot and/or charge later in the same turn.

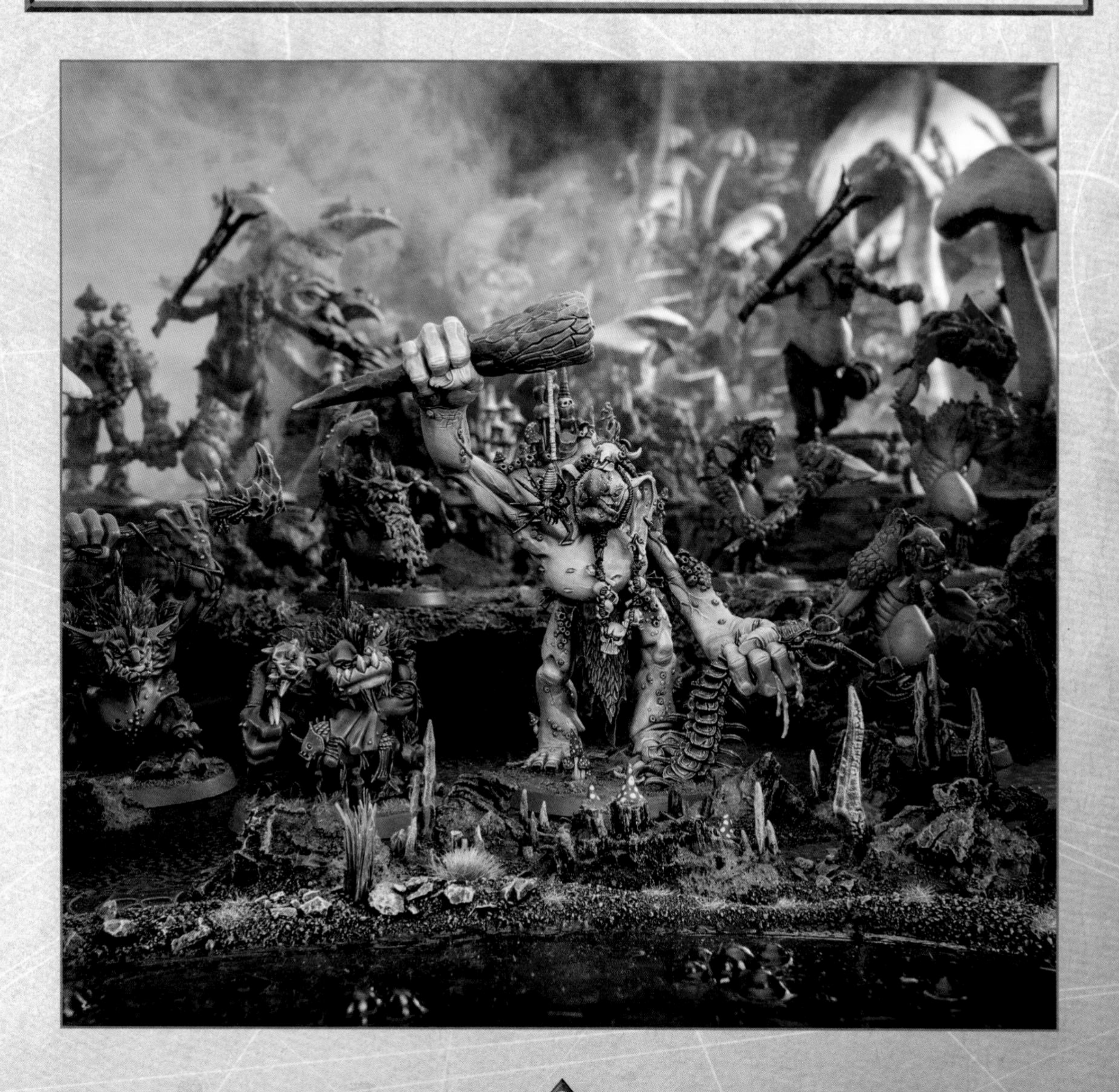

GRIMSCUTTLE TRIBES ALLEGIANCE ABILITIES

If your army is a Gloomspite Gitz army, you can give it the GRIMSCUTTLE keyword. All Gloomspite Gitz units in your army gain that keyword, and you can use the following allegiance abilities in addition to the allegiance abilities in *Battletome: Gloomspite Gitz*.

THE SCUTTLERS STRIKE

GRIMSCUTTLE armies only.

ABILITIES

Deff Grotz of Shyish: *The zealous grots of the Grimscuttle tribes boast of their connection to the Spider God, and they certainly seem to display a knack for channelling its uncanny powers.*

Each time a friendly GRIMSCUTTLE SPIDERFANG unit is affected by a spell or endless spell, you can roll a dice. If you do so, on a 5+, ignore the effects of that spell or endless spell on that unit.

Drawn to the Aetherglow: *The Skitterstrands worshipped by the Grimscuttle tribes have developed a taste for magically charged prey, and they pursue these targets with particular hunger.*

You can re-roll hit rolls for attacks made with melee weapons by friendly SKITTERSTRAND models if the target is a WIZARD or PRIEST.

COMMAND ABILITY

Masters of Feigned Flight: *The Grimscuttle grots are the masters of feigned flight, falling back before returning to attack once more. The fact that such retreats often aren't initially feigned helps a little.*

You can use this command ability at the start of your movement phase. If you do so, pick 1 friendly GRIMSCUTTLE SPIDERFANG unit wholly within 12" of a friendly GRIMSCUTTLE SPIDERFANG HERO. Until your next hero phase, that unit can retreat and still charge later in the same turn.

COMMAND TRAIT

A GRIMSCUTTLE WEBSPINNER SHAMAN general must have the following command trait:

Prophet of da Spider God: *So fervently does this shaman believe in the monstrous deity of the Deff Grotz that when he raises his squeaky voice in prayer, his followers really do seem to be blessed with the Spider God's potent venoms.*

Once per battle, in the combat phase, you can say that this general will unleash their battle cry. If you do so, friendly GRIMSCUTTLE SPIDERFANG models are treated as being affected by the light of the Bad Moon until the end of that phase.

ARTEFACT OF POWER

The first GRIMSCUTTLE SPIDERFANG HERO to receive an artefact of power must be given the Shyishan Spider-sigils.

Shyishan Spider-sigils: *The greatest Grimscuttle bosses daub themselves and their mounts with morbid symbols that strike fear into all those familiar with the scuttling horror of the Deff Grotz.*

Subtract 1 from the Bravery characteristic of enemy units while they are within 6" of the bearer. In addition, add 1 to the Bravery characteristic of friendly GRIMSCUTTLE SPIDERFANG units while they are wholly within 12" of the bearer.

GRIMSCUTTLE WARSCROLL BATTALION
GRIMSCUTTLE SPIDER CLUSTER

ORGANISATION

A Grimscuttle Spider Cluster consists of the following units:

- 2-4 **Grimscuttle Arachnarok Spider** units in any combination

ABILITIES

Monstrous Titans: *The Arachnaroks of Neferatia are possessed of a particularly dark temperament, and they revel in spearing hapless foes on their sharp, agile legs.*

Add 1 to hit rolls for attacks made with melee weapons by units from this battalion.

GRIMSCUTTLE WARSCROLL BATTALION
GRIMSCUTTLE SKITTERSWARM

ORGANISATION

A Grimscuttle Skitterswarm consists of the following units:

- 0-1 **Grimscuttle** Scuttleboss on Gigantic Spider or **Grimscuttle** Webspinner Shaman
- 3+ **Grimscuttle** Spider Riders units

ABILITIES

Through the Cracks They Creep: *Whether outflanking the foe via the use of cunning trap-holes or emerging from the tunnels bored through reality by their allied Skitterstrands, Deff Grotz Spider Riders are adept at striking from unexpected directions.*

At the start of the first battle round, after determining who has the first turn but before the first turn begins, you can pick up to D3 units from this battalion and remove them from the battlefield. If you do so, at the end of your first movement phase, set up those units again wholly within 6" of the edge of the battlefield and more than 9" from any enemy units.

GRIMSCUTTLE WARSCROLL BATTALION
GRIMSCUTTLE NEST

ORGANISATION

A Grimscuttle Nest consists of the following units:

- 2-3 **Grimscuttle** Skitterstrand Arachnaroks

ABILITIES

Reality's Skin-crawlers: *The Skitterstrand Arachnaroks that fight alongside the Grimscuttle tribes are amongst the most cunning of their kind, constantly skittering through the skin of reality to catch their prey off guard.*

In your movement phase, instead of making a normal move with a model from this battalion, you can say that it will tunnel through the web-strewn portals. If you do so, remove that model from the battlefield and set it up again anywhere on the battlefield more than 9" from any enemy units.

• WARSCROLL •

ALARIELLE THE EVERQUEEN

The ground shudders beneath the tread of her gargantuan wardroth beetle as Alarielle leads the Sylvaneth charge. Wherever the goddess's gaze falls, her foes cower, for there is no mercy in the Everqueen's heart towards those who despoil her realm.

MISSILE WEAPONS	Range	Attacks	To Hit	To Wound	Rend	Damage
Spear of Kurnoth	24"	1	2+	2+	-2	✸
MELEE WEAPONS	**Range**	**Attacks**	**To Hit**	**To Wound**	**Rend**	**Damage**
Talon of the Dwindling	1"	4	3+	4+	-	1
Great Antlers	1"	4	3+	2+	-2	✸

DAMAGE TABLE			
Wounds Suffered	**Move**	**Spear of Kurnoth**	**Great Antlers**
0-3	16"	6	5
4-6	15"	5	4
7-8	14"	4	3
9-10	13"	3	2
11+	12"	2	1

DESCRIPTION

Alarielle the Everqueen is a named character that is a single model. She is armed with the Spear of Kurnoth and the Talon of the Dwindling. If Alarielle the Everqueen is included in a Sylvaneth army, Alarielle the Everqueen is treated as a general in addition to the model that is chosen to be the army general.

MOUNT: Alarielle's wardroth beetle attacks with its Great Antlers.

FLY: This model can fly.

ABILITIES

Lifebloom: *Alarielle calls upon the restorative energies of Ghyran to breathe fresh vitality into those who serve her.*

In your hero phase, you can heal up to 2D6 wounds allocated to this model. In addition, you can heal D3 wounds allocated to each other friendly **SYLVANETH** unit wholly within 30" of this model (roll separately for each unit).

Living Battering Ram: *A charging wardroth beetle tramples all in its path.*

Roll a dice for each enemy unit that is within 1" of this model after this model has made a charge move. On a 1, nothing happens. On a 2-5, that unit suffers D3 mortal wounds. On a 6, that unit suffers D6 mortal wounds.

Soul Amphorae: *Alarielle scatters the precious magical pollens within her soul amphorae, seeding the battlefield with new life.*

Once per battle, at the end of your movement phase, you can summon 1 of the following units to the battlefield:

- 1 unit of up to 20 Dryads
- 1 unit of up to 10 Tree-Revenants
- 1 unit of up to 10 Spite-Revenants
- 1 unit of up to 3 Kurnoth Hunters
- 1 Branchwych
- 1 Treelord

The summoned unit is added to your army, and it must be set up wholly within 9" of this model and more than 9" from any enemy units.

Swirling Glowspites: *Whenever Alarielle takes to the air upon her fronded wings, her wardroth beetle shatters into a million swirling glowspites.*

This model can retreat and still shoot and/or charge later in the same turn.

Talon of the Dwindling: *A mere touch from the Talon of the Dwindling is enough to wither the spirit and atrophy the body.*

Roll a dice each time a wound inflicted by this model's Talon of the Dwindling is allocated to an enemy model and not negated. On a 6, that enemy model is slain. On a 1-5, that wound is negated.

MAGIC

Alarielle the Everqueen is a **WIZARD**. She can attempt to cast 3 spells in your hero phase and attempt to unbind 3 spells in the enemy hero phase. She knows the Arcane Bolt, Mystic Shield and Metamorphosis spells. In addition, she knows all of the spells from the Lore of the Deepwood (see *Battletome: Sylvaneth*).

Metamorphosis: *With a wrathful glare from the Everqueen, the enemy is turned to wood.*

Metamorphosis has a casting value of 7. If successfully cast, pick 1 enemy unit within 16" of the caster and visible to them, and roll a number of dice equal to the casting roll. For each 3+, that unit suffers 1 mortal wound.

In addition, if that unit is destroyed by the mortal wounds caused by this spell, before removing the last slain model from play, you can set up 1 **AWAKENED WYLDWOOD** terrain feature wholly within 12" of that slain model, more than 1" from any other models, terrain features or objectives, and add it to your army.

COMMAND ABILITIES

Ghyran's Wrath: *The fury of the reborn Everqueen knows no bounds.*

If this model is in your army, you can use this command ability at the start of the combat phase. If you do so, you can re-roll wound rolls of 1 for attacks made by friendly **SYLVANETH** units wholly within 14" of this model until the end of that phase.

KEYWORDS	ORDER, SYLVANETH, MONSTER, HERO, WIZARD, ALARIELLE THE EVERQUEEN

WARSONG REVENANT

The Warsong Revenants are few in number, but the Spirit Song they carry can cause the lands themselves to come alive. Their odd, skirling music is a balm to the Sylvaneth and a deadly bane to their foes.

MELEE WEAPONS	Range	Attacks	To Hit	To Wound	Rend	Damage
Spearing Vines	3"	5	3+	3+	-1	2

DESCRIPTION

A Warsong Revenant is a single model armed with Spearing Vines.

FLY: This model can fly.

ABILITIES

Alarielle's Song: *To the Sylvaneth, the sound that emanates from a Warsong Revenant's flute is sweet and uplifting. To their foes, it is a sonic assault of devastating potency.*

Add 1 to the Bravery characteristic of friendly SYLVANETH units while they are wholly within 12" of any models with this ability, and subtract 1 from the Bravery characteristic of enemy units while they are within 12" of any models with this ability.

Arboreal Cloak: *The seemingly flimsy cloak of leaves worn by a Warsong Revenant shields it with life-giving energy.*

Roll a dice each time you allocate a wound or mortal wound to this model. On a 4+, that wound or mortal wound is negated.

Wyldwood Revenants: *Warsong Revenants are bound to nature and draw strength from nearby forests.*

Add 1 to casting, dispelling and unbinding rolls for this model while it is within 9" of any AWAKENED WYLDWOODS.

MAGIC

This model is a WIZARD. It can attempt to cast 2 spells in your hero phase and attempt to unbind 1 spell in the enemy hero phase. It knows the Arcane Bolt, Mystic Shield and Unleash Swarm of Spites spells. In addition, it knows all of the spells from the Lore of the Deepwood (see *Battletome: Sylvaneth*).

Unleash Swarm of Spites: *The Warsong Revenant summons a large swarm of malicious spites that spiral outwards to attack those who have displeased it.*

Unleash Swarm of Spites has a casting value of 7. If successfully cast, roll a number of dice equal to the casting roll for each enemy unit within 9" of the caster. For each 5+, that enemy unit suffers 1 mortal wound.

KEYWORDS	ORDER, SYLVANETH, HERO, WIZARD, WARSONG REVENANT

• SCENERY WARSCROLL •

AWAKENED WYLDWOOD

When the Wyldwoods of the Sylvaneth stir, enemies of the natural order must be on their guard. The awakened spirits that dwell within these ancient groves are roused to terrible fury by intrusions into their domain. They seek every chance to prey upon those foolish enough to stray beneath their shadowed boughs.

DESCRIPTION

When you choose a Sylvaneth army, you can include 1 Awakened Wyldwood terrain feature. In addition, you may be able to add additional Awakened Wyldwood terrain features to the battlefield after the battle has started.

Each Awakened Wyldwood consists of 1-3 scenery pieces. After territories have been determined, you can set up any friendly Awakened Wyldwood terrain features taken as part of your army wholly within your own territory, more than 3" from all other terrain features and objectives. If both players can set up terrain features after territories have been determined, the players must roll off, and the winner chooses who sets up their terrain features first.

Any abilities that allow you to add Awakened Wyldwood terrain features to the battlefield will tell you how to set them up. In addition, they must be set up more than 3" from all other terrain features and objectives.

If an Awakened Wyldwood has more than 1 scenery piece, each piece must be set up touching all of the other pieces to form a single circle with an area of open ground inside the circle. The area of open ground inside the circle is considered to be part of the Awakened Wyldwood terrain feature.

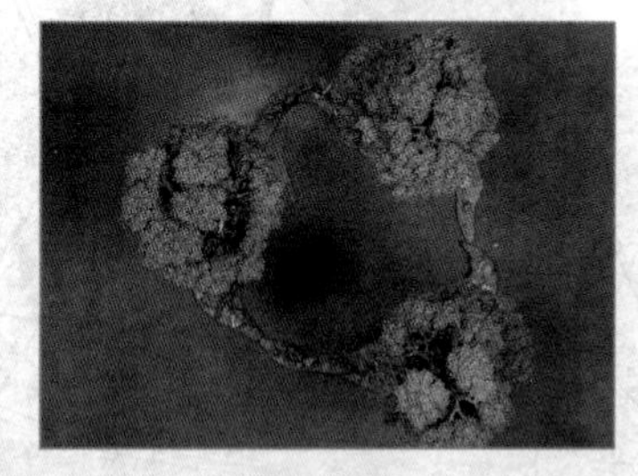

SCENERY RULES

Overgrown Wilderness: *It is only possible to see a few yards into these foreboding thickets.*

Visibility between 2 models is blocked if a straight line 1mm wide drawn between the closest points of the 2 models passes across more than 3" of an AWAKENED WYLDWOOD. Visibility to or from models with a Wounds characteristic of 10 or more is not blocked by an AWAKENED WYLDWOOD. Visibility from units with the SYLVANETH keyword is not blocked by an AWAKENED WYLDWOOD.

Vengeful Forest Spirits: *The spirits within an awakened wyldwood are easily angered by trespassers into their domain – even more so when arcane powers are being used nearby.*

At the end of the charge phase, roll a dice for each unit that does not have the SYLVANETH keyword that is within 1" of an AWAKENED WYLDWOOD. Add 2 to the roll if any WIZARDS or endless spells are within 6" of that AWAKENED WYLDWOOD. On a 6+, that unit suffers D3 mortal wounds.

KEYWORDS	SCENERY, AWAKENED WYLDWOOD

WARSCROLL BATTALION

DRYCHA'S SPITEGROVE

Drycha Hamadreth hates all sentient beings that are not Sylvaneth, thereby embodying the harshest side of all of Ghyran's many seasons. When given free rein to vent her fury, she gathers her most trusted revenants to her side and unleashes a storm of whipping, tearing vengeance against those who would trespass on sacred lands. Amidst a cloud of biting, stinging spites, their iron-hard talons tear the hearts from those they catch.

ORGANISATION

- Drycha Hamadreth
- 2 Spite-Revenants units

ABILITIES

The Spitegrove: *The Spite-Revenants that follow Drycha hate all other forms of life. As they attack in a thrashing frenzy of sharpened limbs, a cloud of voracious spites surrounds them and bites ferociously at the foe.*

The Cruel Talons and Fangs used by units in this battalion have a Rend characteristic of -1 instead of '-'.

• WARSCROLL •

DEXCESSA

THE TALON OF SLAANESH

Dexcessa considers themselves to be the right hand of Slaanesh, made manifest in the realms to sunder and unpick the alliances of his enemies. If that means that they can revel in the glorious, ever-escalating excess of battle, so much the better.

MELEE WEAPONS	Range	Attacks	To Hit	To Wound	Rend	Damage
Scourge of Slaanesh	3"	4	2+	3+	-1	2
Impaling Talons	1"	2	3+	3+	-2	2

DESCRIPTION

Dexcessa, the Talon of Slaanesh, is a named character that is a single model. They are armed with a Scourge of Slaanesh and Impaling Talons.

FLY: This model can fly.

ABILITIES

Fleeting Dance of Death: *Dexcessa rarely stays locked in combat in one place for long, flitting swiftly all over the battlefield and bringing death where they alight.*

This model can run or retreat and still charge later in the same turn.

Joyous Battle Fury: *Once Dexcessa begins to fight, they become invigorated by the glorious thrill of combat.*

After this model has fought for the first time, at the start of each battle round, add 1 to the Attacks characteristics of this model's weapons for the rest of the battle. This effect is cumulative.

Mesmerising Lepidoptera: *Dexcessa's multifaceted wings create a hypnotic effect that distracts their foes.*

Subtract 1 from hit rolls for attacks that target this model.

Sceptre of Slaanesh: *The sceptre of Slaanesh allows the bearer to demand total, unthinking obedience from Slaanesh's daemonic minions.*

Do not take battleshock tests for friendly **SLAANESH DAEMON** units wholly within 12" of this model.

In addition, once per turn, this model can issue a command to a friendly **SLAANESH DAEMON** unit without a command point being spent.

KEYWORDS CHAOS, DAEMON, SLAANESH, HEDONITE, MONSTER, HERO, DEXCESSA

• WARSCROLL •

SYNESSA

THE VOICE OF SLAANESH

Where their sibling adores physical excess, Synessa's power lies in the manipulation of the mind. Even a glance at their splendour leaves those nearby enthralled, and the daemons of Slaanesh enter raptures of obedience at their every word.

MISSILE WEAPONS	Range	Attacks	To Hit	To Wound	Rend	Damage
Staff of Slaanesh	18"	1	See below			
MELEE WEAPONS	**Range**	**Attacks**	**To Hit**	**To Wound**	**Rend**	**Damage**
Impaling Talons	1"	3	3+	3+	-2	2

DESCRIPTION

Synessa, the Voice of Slaanesh, is a named character that is a single model. They are armed with the Staff of Slaanesh and Impaling Talons.

FLY: This model can fly.

ABILITIES

Mesmerising Lepidoptera: *Synessa's multifaceted wings create a hypnotic effect that distracts their foes.*

Subtract 1 from hit rolls for attacks that target this model.

Staff of Slaanesh: *Those who are struck by the bolts of energy unleashed by this staff find themselves tearing at their own flesh in an ecstasy of self-mutilation.*

Do not pick a target or use the attack sequence for an attack made with this model's Staff of Slaanesh. Instead, pick 1 enemy unit within range of this model's Staff of Slaanesh and visible to them. The opposing player must roll a dice for that unit.

If the roll is less than that unit's Save characteristic but not a 6, that unit suffers D6 mortal wounds. If the roll is equal to or greater than that unit's Save characteristic but not a 6, that unit suffers D3 mortal wounds. On a 6, nothing happens.

The Voice of Slaanesh: *Synessa can direct the words that they utter to reach the ear of whomever they want to hear them.*

If this model issues a command to 1 friendly unit, that friendly unit can be anywhere on the battlefield as long as it is visible to this model (the range of the command ability does not apply). If this model issues a command to more than 1 friendly unit, 1 of those friendly units can be anywhere on the battlefield as long as it is visible to this model (the range of the command ability still applies to the other units).

In addition, if this model successfully casts Whispers of Doubt (see right) or Pavane of Slaanesh (see *Battletome: Hedonites of Slaanesh*), the HERO affected by the spell can be anywhere on the battlefield as long as that HERO is visible to this model (the range of the spell does not apply).

MAGIC

Synessa, the Voice of Slaanesh, is a WIZARD. They can attempt to cast 1 spell in your hero phase and attempt to unbind 1 spell in the enemy hero phase. They know the Arcane Bolt, Mystic Shield and Whispers of Doubt spells. In addition, they know all of the spells from the Lore of Slaanesh, the Forbidden Sorceries of Slaanesh and the Lore of Pain and Pleasure (see *Battletome: Hedonites of Slaanesh*).

Whispers of Doubt: *The caster whispers words that reveal the enemy's darkest desires, breaking their concentration and leaving them vulnerable to attack.*

Whispers of Doubt has a casting value of 6. If successfully cast, pick 1 enemy HERO within 3" of the caster and visible to them, and roll 3D6. If the roll is equal to or greater than that HERO's Bravery characteristic, add 1 to hit rolls for attacks that target that HERO until your next hero phase.

KEYWORDS	CHAOS, DAEMON, SLAANESH, HEDONITE, MONSTER, HERO, SYNESSA

WARSCROLL BATTALION

THE EXQUISITE PURSUIT

The Exquisite Pursuit are a strange and unsettling group of hunters, yet hunters they are nonetheless. Led by the Heralds Luxion and Vresca, it is their fervent desire to hound their prey to the edge of madness and beyond. Surrounded by their hunting pack of Fiends and Seekers, the Heralds are borne upon the writhing, tentacular carriage of their prized Mirror of Twisted Truths. At hunt's end, those who catch sight of themselves in the mirror are driven to madness by what they behold – and then the frenzied killing begins…

ORGANISATION

- The Contorted Epitome (Luxion and Vresca)
- 1 Fiends unit
- 1 Seekers unit

The Contorted Epitome in this battalion is a Unique named character.

ABILITIES

The Mirror of Twisted Truths: *Those who see their own reflection in the mirror held aloft by Luxion and Vresca are reduced to gibbering insanity in moments, tearing at their fellows before finally expiring.*

In your shooting phase, you can either pick 1 enemy unit that is within 3" of Luxion and Vresca or pick 1 enemy unit that is within 12" of the Luxion and Vresca and more than 3" from any other units in your army. Roll a dice for each model in that unit. If that unit has a Wounds characteristic of 1, for each 6, that unit suffers 1 mortal wound. If that unit has a Wounds characteristic of more than 1, for each 6, that unit suffers D3 mortal wounds.

FREE CITY OF EXCELSIS

When you pick the Cities of Sigmar allegiance for your army, you can say it will be an Excelsis army. If you do so, you must give it the **Excelsis** city keyword instead of one from the list in *Battletome: Cities of Sigmar*. If a model already has a city keyword on its warscroll, it cannot gain the **Excelsis** keyword (you can still include the model in your army but you cannot use the allegiance abilities for its city).

The army is still considered to be a Cities of Sigmar army and can use the Ways of the Free Peoples battle traits unless stated otherwise.

EXCELSIS BATTLE TRAITS

CITY OF SECRETS

Excelsis armies only.

THE COAST OF TUSKS

The port-city of Excelsis is located in a bay on the Coast of Tusks in the Realm of Beasts.

An Excelsis army must be from Ghur.

GIFT OF PROPHECY

To hold a shard of the Spear of Mallus is to see visions of futures yet to come. By interpreting these prophecies, scryers can capitalise on them.

Once per phase, when you pick a friendly unit to shoot or fight, you can say that the attack has been prophesied. If you do so, roll a dice. On a 1, subtract 1 from hit rolls for attacks made by that unit in that phase. On a 2-6, add 1 to hit rolls for attacks made by that unit in that phase.

COMMAND ABILITY

Riposte: *Excelsis commanders are adept at anticipating the enemy's attacks, warning their warriors so they can deliver a deadly riposte.*

You can use this command ability at the start of the combat phase. If you do so, pick 1 friendly **Excelsis** unit wholly within 12" of a friendly **Excelsis Hero**. If the unmodified save roll for an attack that targets that unit in that combat phase is 6, the attacking unit suffers 1 mortal wound after all of its attacks have been resolved.

EXCELSIS COMMAND TRAITS

MASTERS OF INTRIGUE

Excelsis generals only.

D3	Command Trait
1	**Cunning Foe:** *This general uses subterfuge to befuddle their enemies.* This general can retreat and still charge in the same turn. If they do so, until the end of the turn, add 1 to hit rolls for attacks made by this general and subtract 1 from hit rolls for attacks that target them.
2	**In the Right Place:** *This general's troops appear where they are needed.* At the start of the first battle round, you can pick D3 friendly units and set them up again. Any restrictions in the set-up instructions for the battleplan being used still apply.
3	**Darkest Secrets:** *This general exploits their enemy's innermost secrets.* At the start of the combat phase, you can pick 1 enemy **Hero** within 3" of this general. That **Hero** cannot use command abilities until the next combat phase (any already used still apply).

EXCELSIS ARTEFACTS OF POWER

SECRET HEIRLOOMS

Excelsis Heroes only.

D3 Artefact

1 Glimmering: *Flinders of the Spear of Mallus are traded as 'glimmerings', each yielding visions of events yet to come.*

Once per battle, before you make a hit or wound roll for an attack made by the bearer, a save roll for an attack that targets the bearer, or a run or charge roll for the bearer, you can say that you will foretell the result of the roll. If you do so, you must choose the result of the roll. The result chosen for a D6 roll must be a whole number from 1 to 6, and the result chosen for a 2D6 roll must be a whole number from 2 to 12. The result cannot be re-rolled, but any modifiers are applied to it as normal.

2 Rockjaws: *When thrown at the foe, this steel-sprung trap will clamp down tightly enough to penetrate metal, flesh and bone.*

In your shooting phase, you can pick 1 enemy unit within 8" of the bearer that is visible to them and roll a dice. On a 3+, that unit suffers D3 mortal wounds.

3 Gryph-feather Charm: *Rarely do these feathers fall, and those who manage to acquire one are lucky indeed.*

Subtract 1 from hit rolls for attacks that target the bearer. In addition, add 1" to the bearer's Move characteristic.

EXCELSIS SPELL LORES

You can choose or roll for one of the following spells for each **Wizard** in an Excelsis army.

LORE OF THE GHURISH HEARTLANDS

D3 Spell

1 The Amber Spear: *The wizard conjures a lance of pure amber and hurls it at the foe.*

The Amber Spear has a casting value of 6. If successfully cast, pick a point on the battlefield within 12" of the caster that is visible to them and draw an imaginary straight line 1mm wide between that point and the closest point on the caster's base. Each unit other than the caster that has any models passed across by this line suffers 1 mortal wound.

2 Flock of Doom: *Reaching to the skies, the wizard brings down a swarm of vicious birds to peck and claw at the enemy.*

Flock of Doom has a casting value of 6. If successfully cast, pick 1 enemy unit within 18" of the caster that is visible to them and roll 12 dice. For each 6, that enemy unit suffers 1 mortal wound.

3 Cower: *Transfixing a beast with a steely glare, the wizard briefly binds the creature to their will.*

Cower has a casting value of 6. If successfully cast, pick 1 enemy **Monster** within 12" of the caster that is visible to them and roll 2D6. If the roll is higher than that **Monster**'s Bravery characteristic, that **Monster** cannot make a charge move in your opponent's next turn.

• WARSCROLL •

DORALIA VEN DENST

Despite her youth, Doralia ven Denst is a renowned agent of the Order of Azyr. Not only a hunter of witches and warlocks, she is a specialist in dispelling the endless spells they unleash, banishing them with consecrated blade and crossbow bolt alike.

MISSILE WEAPONS	Range	Attacks	To Hit	To Wound	Rend	Damage
Crossbow	24"	1	3+	3+	-2	2
MELEE WEAPONS	**Range**	**Attacks**	**To Hit**	**To Wound**	**Rend**	**Damage**
Witch Hunter's Sword	1"	3	3+	3+	-1	1

DESCRIPTION

Doralia ven Denst is a named character that is a single model. She is armed with a Crossbow and Witch Hunter's Sword.

ABILITIES

Grim Resolve: *Witch hunters are tenacious opponents, ignoring the pain of wounds that would fell a lesser person.*

Roll a dice each time you allocate a wound or mortal wound to this model. On a 5+, that wound or mortal wound is negated.

Sureshot: *Doralia rarely misses when she takes up position with her crossbow, each shot putting a bolt between the eyes of another opponent.*

Add 1 to the Attacks characteristic of this model's Crossbow and add 1 to hit rolls for attacks made with this model's Crossbow if this model has not made a move in the same turn.

Weapons of Banishment: *Inscribed with the holy writ of Sigmar and inlaid with nullstone and silver, Doralia's anti-thaumic crossbow bolts and consecrated blade are anathema to spellcasters and their works, banishing all forms of arcane energy in a flash.*

Double the Damage characteristic of an attack made with this model's weapons if the target of that attack is a WIZARD or DAEMON.

In addition, when this model fights or shoots, you can choose an endless spell to be the target of any of its attacks. If you do so, roll a dice to see if that attack scores a hit. If it does, do not make a wound or save roll. Instead, roll 2D6. If the roll is greater than the casting value of that endless spell, that endless spell is dispelled.

KEYWORDS ORDER, HUMAN, CITIES OF SIGMAR, HERO, WITCH HUNTER, DORALIA VEN DENST

WARSCROLL

GALEN VEN DENST

As an agent of Azyr, Galen ven Denst has executed hundreds of Chaos cultists and living dead over the course of his career. His stoicism and agility is impressive, his skill with spell-banishing pistol and runic broadsword all the more so.

MISSILE WEAPONS	Range	Attacks	To Hit	To Wound	Rend	Damage
Pistol	9"	3	3+	3+	-1	1
MELEE WEAPONS	**Range**	**Attacks**	**To Hit**	**To Wound**	**Rend**	**Damage**
Broadsword	1"	6	3+	3+	-1	1

DESCRIPTION

Galen ven Denst is a named character that is a single model. He is armed with a Pistol and Broadsword.

ABILITIES

Grim Resolve: *Witch hunters are tenacious opponents, ignoring the pain of wounds that would fell a lesser person.*

Roll a dice each time you allocate a wound or mortal wound to this model. On a 5+, that wound or mortal wound is negated.

Agile Opponent: *Galen is always on the move, fighting with the utmost balance and surety.*

This model can retreat and still shoot and/or charge in the same turn.

Weapons of Banishment: *Inlaid with nullstone and silver, Galen's pistol shot and broadsword blade are anathema to spellcasters and their works, banishing all forms of arcane energy in a flash.*

Double the Damage characteristic of an attack made with this model's weapons if the target of that attack is a WIZARD or DAEMON.

In addition, when this model fights or shoots, you can choose an endless spell to be the target of any of its attacks. If you do so, roll a dice to see if that attack scores a hit. If it does, do not make a wound or save roll. Instead, roll 2D6. If the roll is greater than the casting value of that endless spell, that endless spell is dispelled.

KEYWORDS ORDER, HUMAN, CITIES OF SIGMAR, HERO, WITCH HUNTER, GALEN VEN DENST

• WARSCROLL •

LORD KROAK

Despite his deathly state, Lord Kroak is the most powerful of all slann. The venerable Relic Priest appears unbidden when the Great Plan is most imperilled, the foes of the Seraphon laid to waste through an onslaught of arcane power.

MELEE WEAPONS	Range	Attacks	To Hit	To Wound	Rend	Damage
Azyrite Force Barrier	3"	See below	3+	3+	-1	1

DESCRIPTION

Lord Kroak is a named character that is a single model. He is armed with an Azyrite Force Barrier.

FLY: Lord Kroak can fly.

ABILITIES

Arcane Vassal: *A Slann Starmaster can channel the power of a spell through one of their followers.*

When this model attempts to cast a spell, before making the casting roll, you can pick either 1 friendly **SKINK WIZARD** that is within 12" of this model or 1 friendly **ORACLE** anywhere on the battlefield. If you do so and the spell is successfully cast and not unbound, you must measure the range and visibility for the spell from that **SKINK WIZARD** or **ORACLE**.

Azyrite Force Barrier: *Lord Kroak's desiccated form is protected by a crackling energy field that blasts enemies who dare come close.*

The Attacks characteristic of an Azyrite Force Barrier is equal to the number of enemy models within 3" of the attacking model when the number of attacks made with the weapon is determined. Count each enemy **MONSTER** as 5 models for the purpose of this rule.

Dead for Innumerable Ages: *Lord Kroak is no longer alive in the conventional sense; his ancient and withered form is preserved only by his indomitable spirit. As such, he is almost immune to all but the most devastating attacks.*

At the end of each phase, if any wounds or mortal wounds are allocated to this model, roll 3D6 and add the number of wounds and mortal wounds allocated to this model to the roll. On a 20+, this model is slain. On any other roll, all wounds and mortal wounds allocated to this model are healed.

Designer's Note: *If Lord Kroak suffers 18 or more wounds or mortal wounds before the end of a phase, he is immediately slain and no dice roll is made at the end of the phase.*

Impeccable Foresight: *Lord Kroak casts his mind into the future, reading the threads of destiny as easily as a mortal would read a map.*

At the start of your hero phase, roll 3 dice for this model. For each 4+, you receive 1 command point.

Supreme Master of Order: *The slann are among the greatest wizards in existence, but Lord Kroak is mighty even in comparison to others of his kind.*

Add 2 to casting, dispelling and unbinding rolls for this model. In addition, this model can attempt to unbind enemy spells that are cast anywhere on the battlefield and attempt to dispel endless spells anywhere on the battlefield.

MAGIC

Lord Kroak is a **WIZARD**. He can attempt to cast 4 spells in your hero phase and attempt to unbind 4 spells in the enemy hero phase. He knows the Arcane Bolt, Mystic Shield, Celestial Deliverance and Comet's Call spells. In addition, he knows all of the spells from the Lore of Celestial Domination (see *Battletome: Seraphon*).

Celestial Deliverance: *Lord Kroak's palanquin quivers with barely contained force before unleashing ruination on the enemies of the Seraphon.*

The caster can attempt to cast this spell up to 3 times in the same hero phase. Celestial Deliverance has a casting value of 7 the first time it is attempted in a phase, a casting value of 8 the second time it is attempted in a phase, and a casting value of 9 the third time it is attempted in a phase.

Each time this spell is successfully cast, pick up to 3 different enemy units within 10" of the caster and visible to them, and roll 1 dice for each unit you pick. On a 2+, that unit suffers D3 mortal wounds. If that unit is a **CHAOS DAEMON** unit, on a 2+, it suffers 3 mortal wounds instead of D3 mortal wounds.

Comet's Call: *His consciousness soaring up to the heavens, the caster summons a cluster of comets before casting them into the enemy's ranks.*

Comet's Call has a casting value of 7. If successfully cast, you can pick up to D3 different enemy units anywhere on the battlefield. Each of those units suffers D3 mortal wounds (roll separately for each). If the casting roll was 10+, pick up to D6 different enemy units instead of up to D3.

COMMAND ABILITIES

Supreme Gift from the Heavens: *At Lord Kroak's command, his followers are wrapped in a mantle of Azyrite energy, allowing them to disregard the natural laws that govern the Mortal Realms.*

You can use this command ability in your hero phase. If you do so, pick up to D3 friendly **SERAPHON** units wholly within 18" of a friendly model with this command ability. Until your next hero phase, those units can fly and you can add 1 to save rolls for attacks made with missile weapons that target those units. You can only use this command ability once per hero phase.

KEYWORDS	ORDER, SERAPHON, SLANN, HERO, WIZARD, STARMASTER, LORD KROAK

THE SKAVENTIDE

If your army is a Skaventide army, you can use the new Hidden Weapon Teams battle trait below in addition to any other battle traits you can use. You can also use the Clans Moulder Mutations allegiance ability shown on these pages.

BATTLE TRAITS

TEACHINGS OF THE HORNED RAT

HIDDEN WEAPON TEAMS

Clans Skryre weapon teams often lurk unseen amongst the ranks of large formations of Clanrats and Stormvermin, only revealing themselves once they are close enough to use the weapons that they carry.

When you select a **WEAPON TEAM** unit other than a **WARP GRINDER** to be part of your army, you can pick 1 friendly unit of **CLANRATS** or **STORMVERMIN** that has 10 or more models and is already part of your army to be the unit in which that **WEAPON TEAM** unit is hiding. Record this information on a piece of paper. Do not set up the **WEAPON TEAM** unit until it is revealed as described next. You can hide up to 1 **WEAPON TEAM** unit in a **CLANRATS** or **STORMVERMIN** unit for every 10 models in that **CLANRATS** or **STORMVERMIN** unit.

At the start of your shooting phase, you can reveal 1 or more hidden **WEAPON TEAM** units. If you do so, set up each hidden **WEAPON TEAM** unit wholly within 3" of the unit it was hiding in and more than 3" from any enemy units. **WEAPON TEAM** units can shoot in the turn in which they are revealed as long as the unit they were hiding in did not run in the same turn (it could have retreated).

In addition, at the end of your charge phase, you can reveal 1 or more hidden **WEAPON TEAM** units that were hiding in a unit that made a charge move in that phase. If you do so, set up each hidden **WEAPON TEAM** unit wholly within 3" of the unit it was hiding in (it can be set up within 3" of any enemy units and can fight in the following combat phase).

Hidden **WEAPON TEAM** units are destroyed if the unit they are hiding in is destroyed before they are revealed.

CLANS MOULDER MUTATIONS

If a Skaventide army includes any **FIGHTING BEAST** units, 1 of those **FIGHTING BEAST** units can have a Clans Moulder mutation.

In addition, when you pick a **FIGHTING BEAST** unit to benefit from the Prized Creations battle trait at the start of the first battle round (see page 67 of *Battletome: Skaven*), you can choose for it to have a Clans Moulder mutation instead of adding D3 to its Wounds characteristic and re-rolling hit rolls of 1.

Declare which **FIGHTING BEAST** unit will have the Clans Moulder mutation and then choose or roll for a mutation from the appropriate table. The same **FIGHTING BEAST** unit cannot have more than 1 Clans Moulder mutation, and an army may not include duplicates of the same mutation.

HIDEOUS ABOMINATIONS

HELL PIT ABOMINATIONS only.

D6	Mutation
1	**Toughened Sinews:** *The muscles and tendons of this hulking creature are unnaturally strong and tough.* This **HELL PIT ABOMINATION** has a Wounds characteristic of 14 and a Save characteristic of 4+.
2	**Lumbering Behemoth:** *This horrifying creation marches steadily towards the foe, letting nothing slow its pace.* This **HELL PIT ABOMINATION** has a Move characteristic of 7". In addition, charge rolls for this **HELL PIT ABOMINATION** are automatically a 7 (do not roll the dice).
3	**Quivering Bulk:** *The flesh of this monstrosity is horribly distended.* Add 1 to each dice roll you make for this **HELL PIT ABOMINATION**'s Avalanche of Flesh ability.
4	**Accelerated Regeneration:** *Any injuries this creature suffers heal with terrifying swiftness.* You can use this **HELL PIT ABOMINATION**'s Regenerating Monstrosity ability in the enemy hero phase as well as in your hero phase.
5	**Best-best Warpstone Spikes:** *The warpstone spikes driven into this abomination's flesh are of the highest possible quality, enhancing its resistance to the arcane and imbuing its attacks with deadly radiation.* You can re-roll the dice when you use this **HELL PIT ABOMINATION**'s Warpstone Spikes ability. In addition, you can re-roll wound rolls of 1 for attacks made with melee weapons by this **HELL PIT ABOMINATION**.
6	**Never-never Die-die:** *This strain of abomination is exceptionally difficult to destroy.* You can re-roll the dice when you use this **HELL PIT ABOMINATION**'s Too Horrible To Die ability.

BIG-BIG RAT OGORS

RAT OGORS only.

D3	Mutation
1	**Toughened Sinews:** *The muscles and tendons of these hulking creatures are unnaturally strong and tough.* This **RAT OGOR** unit has a Wounds characteristic of 6 and a Save characteristic of 4+.
2	**Insanely Rabid:** *This form of Rat Ogor is extremely ferocious.* This **RAT OGOR** unit's Tearing Claws, Blades and Fangs have an Attacks characteristic of 6. In addition, you can re-roll charge rolls for this **RAT OGOR** unit.
3	**Accelerated Metabolism:** *These creatures have a vastly accelerated metabolic rate; they move with remarkable speed and any injuries they suffer heal in an instant.* This **RAT OGOR** unit has a Move characteristic of 8". In addition, you can heal D3 wounds allocated to this **RAT OGOR** unit in your hero phase.

WARSCROLL BATTALION

RATTACHAK'S DOOM-COVEN

The Warlock Bombardier Rattachak is known for his obsession with fire, up to and sometimes including being on fire himself. He uses incendiary doomrockets that can set alight everything around them upon detonation, and he ensures that the Stormfiends that escort him to battle are amped up in order to cause the absolute maximum destruction with each volley.

ORGANISATION

- 1 Warlock Bombardier (Rattachak)
- 1 Warp Lightning Cannon
- 1 Stormfiends unit

The Warlock Bombardier in this battalion is a Unique named character.

ABILITIES

Rattachak's More-more-more Doomrocket: *Rattachak has spent countless hours and suffered no small amount of personal injury refining the doomrockets he uses in battle and improving the explosive output of the shock gauntlets used by his Stormfiend bodyguards.*

You can re-roll hit rolls for attacks made with Rattachak's Doomrocket and add 1 to that weapon's Damage characteristic. In addition, add 1 to the Damage characteristic of Shock Gauntlets used by the **STORMFIENDS** unit in this battalion while it is wholly within 12" of Rattachak.

WARSCROLL BATTALION

THE BUTCHER-HERD

Ghorraghan Khai is known amongst the warherds of Ghyran as a powerful shaman who, with but a touch of his staff, can reduce his foes to dust. Arrogant and determined enough to take his war against all nature to the heart of the Everspring Swathe, he leads a pack of bull-headed monstrosities to battle through bestial vigour and sheer force of will.

ORGANISATION

- 1 Great Bray-Shaman (Ghorraghan Khai)
- 2 Bullgors units
- 1 Ghorgon

The Great Bray-Shaman in this battalion is a Unique named character.

ABILITIES

Ghorraghan's Skull-staff: *Ghorraghan's skull-festooned fetish staff can reduce a foe to dust.*

Add 2 to the Attacks characteristic of Ghorraghan Khai's Fetish Staff. In addition, if the unmodified hit roll for an attack made with Ghorraghan Khai's Fetish Staff is 6, that attack inflicts D3 mortal wounds on the target and the attack sequence ends (do not make a wound or save roll).

Infuse with Chaos Energy: *Long association with Ghorraghan means that the raw chaotic energy that emanates from the Bray-Shaman fills his personal retinue with strength.*

Add 1 to hit rolls for attacks made by WARHERD units in this battalion that are wholly within 12" of Ghorraghan Khai.

COMMAND TRAIT

If Ghorraghan Khai is your army's general, he has the Indomitable Beast command trait from *Battletome: Beasts of Chaos*.

WARPATHS OF THE BEASTHERDS

If your army is a Beasts of Chaos army, you can use the new Primal Instincts battle traits below in addition to any other Primal Instincts battle traits you can use.

BATTLE TRAITS

PRIMAL INSTINCTS

GOR BATTLE FURY

Gors are always eager for battle – never more so than when they ambush an unwary foe.

You can re-roll charge rolls for friendly Gors units if they were reserve units in ambush and have been set up on the battlefield in the same turn.

Designer's Note: *This ability only applies to units that have the Gors warscroll. It does not apply to other units that have the* **Gor** *keyword.*

WARHERD CHARGE

When a Warherd charges into the foe, the enemy are sent flying through the air by the force of the impact.

After a friendly **Warherd** unit makes a charge move, pick 1 enemy unit within 1" of that unit and roll a dice. Add 2 to the roll if that **Warherd** unit is a **Hero** or has more than 3 models. On a 4+, that enemy unit suffers D3 mortal wounds at the end of the charge phase.

RAGING STORM

As lightning arcs down to the battlefield, the Thunderscorn are imbued with renewed vigour while their enemies are riven by lethal crackling energy.

At the end of the combat phase, you can roll a dice for each friendly **Thunderscorn** unit that is on the battlefield. Add 2 to the roll if the **Thunderscorn** unit is a **Hero** or has more than 3 models. On a 4+, you can heal 1 wound allocated to that unit.

Then, roll a dice for each enemy unit within 1" of any friendly **Thunderscorn** units. Add 2 to the roll if any of those **Thunderscorn** units are **Heroes** or if there are more than 3 **Thunderscorn** models within 1" of that unit. On a 4+, that enemy unit suffers 1 mortal wound.

Designer's Note: *If you take a Thunderscorn Stormherd warscroll battalion in your army, do not use the Raging Storm ability on its warscroll. Instead, when using the Raging Storm ability above, you can re-roll the dice roll when determining if any wounds allocated to units from that battalion are healed, then you can re-roll the dice roll when determining if any enemy units within 1" of any units from that battalion suffer 1 mortal wound.*

• WARSCROLL •

BEASTLORD

Savage commanders and ferocious warriors, Beastlords are the alphabeasts of the Brayherds. They exert dominance over their snarling kin through acts of grisly violence and lead ruinous stampedes into the civilised lands.

MELEE WEAPONS	Range	Attacks	To Hit	To Wound	Rend	Damage
Paired Man-ripper Axes	1"	6	3+	3+	-1	1

DESCRIPTION

A Beastlord is a single model armed with Paired Man-ripper Axes.

ABILITIES

Call of Battle: *Beastlords lope swiftly towards the foe, desperate to get to grips with the enemy so that the bloodletting can begin.*

This model can run and still charge later in the same turn.

Grisly Trophy: *With a roar of triumph, the Beastlord raises a severed head into the air.*

If any enemy models are slain by wounds inflicted by this model's attacks in the combat phase, you can add 1 to wound rolls for attacks made by friendly **BRAYHERD** units wholly within 18" of this model until the end of that phase. In addition, if any enemy **HEROES** or **MONSTERS** are slain by wounds inflicted by this model's attacks in the combat phase, you can add 1 to hit rolls for attacks made by friendly **BRAYHERD** units wholly within 18" of this model until the end of that phase. The same unit cannot benefit from this ability more than once per phase.

Hatred of Heroes: *Leaving weaker foes to his followers, a Beastlord reserves his prodigious strength and fury for the greatest of the enemy's champions.*

If the unmodified hit roll for an attack made with this model's Paired Man-ripper Axes that targets a **HERO** is 6, that attack scores 2 hits on the target instead of 1. Make a wound and save roll for each hit.

KEYWORDS CHAOS, GOR, BEASTS OF CHAOS, BRAYHERD, HERO, BEASTLORD

• WARSCROLL •

JABBERSLYTHE

Grotesque conglomerations of monstrous body parts, Jabberslythes lurch forth from their swampy lairs to hunt. Their anarchic form drives those who look upon them to madness, while their corrosive blood melts those foolish enough to attack them.

MISSILE WEAPONS	Range	Attacks	To Hit	To Wound	Rend	Damage
Slythey Tongue	9"	3	3+	3+	-1	1
MELEE WEAPONS	**Range**	**Attacks**	**To Hit**	**To Wound**	**Rend**	**Damage**
Vorpal Claws	1"	6	3+	3+	-2	1
Spiked Tail	3"	1	4+	2+	-2	D3

DESCRIPTION

A Jabberslythe is a single model armed with a Slythey Tongue, Vorpal Claws and a Spiked Tail.

FLY: Jabberslythes can fly.

ABILITIES

Aura of Madness: *Simply being in the presence of a Jabberslythe is enough to drive a warrior mad, causing them to lash out at friend and foe alike.*

Subtract 1 from casting, dispelling and unbinding rolls for enemy **WIZARDS** within 6" of any units in your army with this ability.

In addition, each time an enemy unit within 3" of any units in your army with this ability is chosen to fight, roll 3D6. If the roll is greater than that enemy unit's Bravery characteristic, until the end of that phase, that unit is deranged. Add 1 to the Attacks characteristic of melee weapons used by a unit that is deranged. However, if the unmodified hit roll for an attack made by a unit that is deranged is 1, it suffers 1 mortal wound after all of its attacks have been resolved.

Spurting Bile Blood: *Jabberslythes are filled with deadly acidic blood that can cause horrific burns to those who dare attack them.*

Roll a dice each time a wound inflicted by a melee weapon is allocated to this model and not negated. On a 4+, the attacking unit suffers 1 mortal wound.

KEYWORDS CHAOS, BEASTS OF CHAOS, MONSTERS OF CHAOS, MONSTER, JABBERSLYTHE

PITCHED BATTLE PROFILES

The table below provides points, minimum and maximum unit sizes and battlefield roles for the warscrolls and warscroll battalions in this book, for use in Pitched Battles. Spending the points listed in this table allows you to take a minimum-sized unit with any of its upgrades. Understrength units cost the full amount of points. Larger units are taken in multiples of their minimum unit size; multiply their cost by the same amount as you multiplied their size. If a unit has two points values separated by a slash (e.g. '60/200'), the second value is for a maximum-sized unit. Units that are listed as 'Unique' are named characters and can only be taken once in an army. Updated June 2021; the profiles printed here take precedence over any profiles with an earlier publication date or no publication date.

BEASTS OF CHAOS	UNIT SIZE		POINTS	BATTLEFIELD ROLE	NOTES
WARSCROLL	MIN	MAX			
Beastlord	1	1	95	Leader	
Jabberslythe	1	1	165	Behemoth	
The Butcher-herd	-	-	*140*	*Warscroll Battalion*	*Unique*

CITIES OF SIGMAR	UNIT SIZE		POINTS	BATTLEFIELD ROLE	NOTES
WARSCROLL	MIN	MAX			
Doralia ven Denst	1	1	115	Leader	Unique
Galen ven Denst	1	1	115	Leader	Unique

DESTRUCTION	UNIT SIZE		POINTS	BATTLEFIELD ROLE	NOTES
WARSCROLL	MIN	MAX			
Kragnos, the End of Empires	1	1	760	Leader, Behemoth	Unique

GLOOMSPITE GITZ	UNIT SIZE		POINTS	BATTLEFIELD ROLE	NOTES
WARSCROLL	MIN	MAX			
Moon-biter Squigalanche	-	-	*90*	*Warscroll Battalion*	
Moon-jumper Stampede	-	-	*140*	*Warscroll Battalion*	
Grimscuttle Nest	-	-	*140*	*Warscroll Battalion*	
Grimscuttle Skitterswarm	-	-	*140*	*Warscroll Battalion*	
Grimscuttle Spider Cluster	-	-	*140*	*Warscroll Battalion*	
Stomping Megamob	-	-	*160*	*Warscroll Battalion*	

HEDONITES OF SLAANESH	UNIT SIZE		POINTS	BATTLEFIELD ROLE	NOTES
WARSCROLL	MIN	MAX			
Dexcessa, the Talon of Slaanesh	1	1	280	Leader	Unique
Synessa, the Voice of Slaanesh	1	1	260	Leader	Unique
The Exquisite Pursuit	-	-	*130*	*Warscroll Battalion*	*Unique*

SERAPHON	UNIT SIZE		POINTS	BATTLEFIELD ROLE	NOTES
WARSCROLL	MIN	MAX			
Lord Kroak	1	1	430	Leader	Unique

SKAVENTIDE	UNIT SIZE		POINTS	BATTLEFIELD ROLE	NOTES
WARSCROLL	MIN	MAX			
Rattachak's Doom-coven	-	-	*130*	*Warscroll Battalion*	*Unique*

SYLVANETH	UNIT SIZE		POINTS	BATTLEFIELD ROLE	NOTES
WARSCROLL	MIN	MAX			
Alarielle the Everqueen	1	1	740	Leader, Behemoth	Unique
Warsong Revenant	1	1	275	Leader	
Drycha's Spitegrove	-	-	*120*	*Warscroll Battalion*	*Unique*